CHILDREN'S
ACTIVITY
BIBLE

1st edition, 4th print 2018

Copyright 2014 © Scandinavia Publishing House

Drejervej 15, DK 2400 Copenhagen NV, Denmark

Email: info@sph.as

www.sph.as

Illustrations: José Pérez Montero

Text: L. M. Alex

Activities and layout: Isabelle Gao

Graphic design: Gao Hanyu

Activity editor: Linda Vium

ISBN Hardcover: 9788771325065

ISBN Softcover: 9788771325072

Printed in China

CHILDREN'S ACTIVITY BIBLE

Bible stories retold by L. M. Alex

Illustrated by José Pérez Montero

✴ SCANDINAVIA

Contents

THE OLD TESTAMENT

THE NEW TESTAMENT

THE OLD TESTAMENT

In the Beginning

Genesis 1:1-19

In the beginning, all was dark. But in the darkness, there was God.

God said, "Let there be light!" And there was light. God saw that the light was good. And with that, the first day passed.

God said, "Let there be Heaven, and let there be Earth." And so it was. On Earth, there would be dry land, and there would be seas. A sun would shine for daytime. A moon would shine for night. And all across the sky, stars would sparkle down on Earth.

God said, "Let there be lights high above the Earth."
All across the sky, stars began to twinkle. "Let
these count the seasons and the days and the
years," He said, "and let them help to bring light on
the Earth."

PLANETS' NAMES

Learn about the planets God created. First, unscramble the names of the 8 planets. Then, use the clues to solve the crossword puzzle.

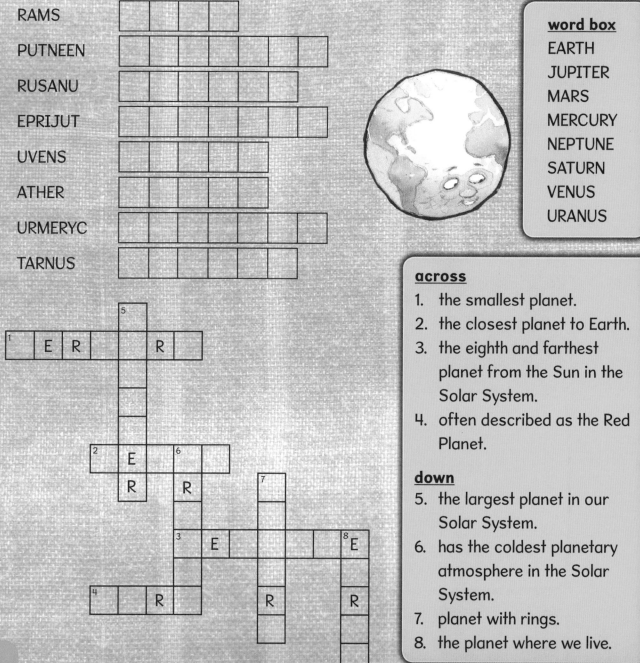

RAMS

PUTNEEN

RUSANU

EPRIJUT

UVENS

ATHER

URMERYC

TARNUS

word box
EARTH
JUPITER
MARS
MERCURY
NEPTUNE
SATURN
VENUS
URANUS

across
1. the smallest planet.
2. the closest planet to Earth.
3. the eighth and farthest planet from the Sun in the Solar System.
4. often described as the Red Planet.

down
5. the largest planet in our Solar System.
6. has the coldest planetary atmosphere in the Solar System.
7. planet with rings.
8. the planet where we live.

PLANETS' POSITIONS

Do you know where the planets are placed in the Solar System? Fill in the letters for each name next to the planet. The letters U and R have been filled in for you.

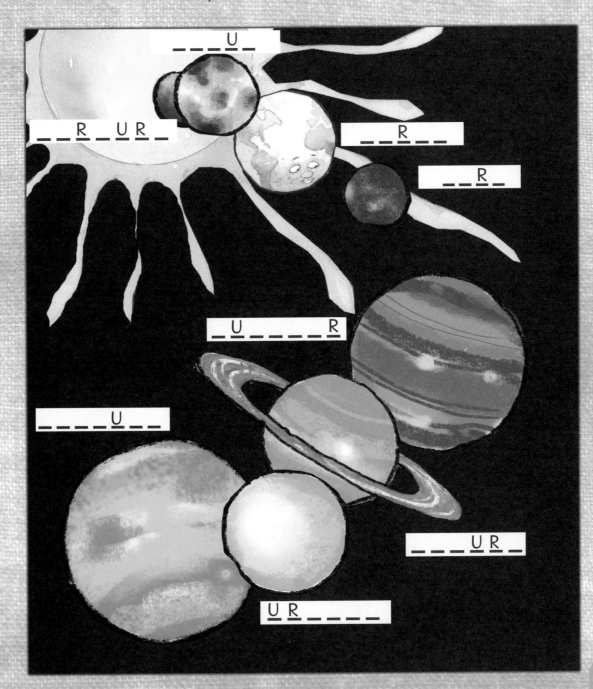

God Brings Life

Genesis 1:20-25

God had made land, and God had made sea. All across the Earth, plants would grow. Each plant would have seeds inside it for making more.

God made animals to live on land. Some would walk. Some would slither. Some would creep. God made animals to fill the seas from giant whales that swam to creatures that scuttled across the sand. Each animal was made from God's imagination. And each was different. Each was beautiful.

God looked at all He had made, and He saw that it was good. On the seventh day of creating, God rested.

PENGUINS

Look at the penguins below. They are all the same except one. Can you find which one?

1 2 3 4

5 6 7 8

GOD MAKES THE ANIMALS

Can you fill in the blanks to complete the story of creation?

God created water and land on E _ _ _ _ .

He filled the oceans with f_ _ _ of amazing shapes and colors.

God made b _ _ _ _ to fly. Then He made a _ _ _ _ _ _ _ to live on land.

ANIMALS AND BIRDS

The names of the animals and birds were cut in half! Draw a line to put them back together.

1

DOL •	• BBIT
ZE •	• PHIN
HOR •	• BRA
RA •	• SE

2

DON •	• VER
CHI •	• KEY
BEA •	• MEL
CA •	• CKEN

3

SNA •	• TRICH
PAN •	• KE
OS •	• GUIN
PEN •	• DA

4

TI •	• COCK
PEA •	• GULL
SEA •	• GER
TUR •	• TLE

Adam & Eve
Genesis 1-3

God had one last creation: *people!* God made a man named Adam. God made a woman named Eve. Together, they were to take care of God's wonderful world.

Adam and Eve got to live in God's beautiful garden, called Eden. It was filled with all sorts of animals. It grew the loveliest trees.

Adam and Eve could eat any fruit except one. They were not to eat the fruit at the middle of the garden. Yet one day, they disobeyed. They ate the fruit God had told them not to. So God would have to send them away. From now on, Adam and Eve would grow their own food.

Yet even still, God watched over them. Even still, God loved them.

THE ANIMALS GET NAMES

The animals all got names, one by one. Can you find 10 differences between these two pictures?

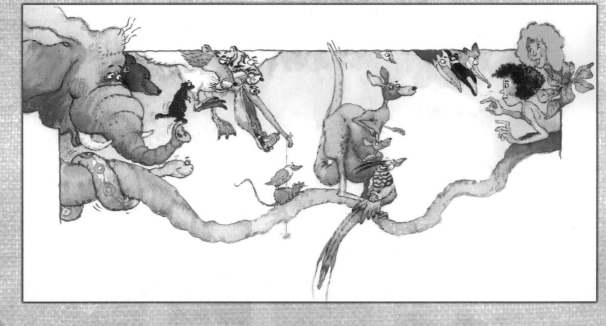

THE GARDEN OF EDEN

Find the 12 hidden words taken from the story of Adam and Eve. They may be up, down, across, backwards, or diagonal.

```
G E F N E L W N A E
W A X C O K O B F N
O R R V E I A R K A
R T E D T D U N M M
L D O A E I E H B O
D E E R T N U N Y W
H R A N I M A L S U
C A S N A K E M Z E
B E A U T I F U L B
W D E Y E B O S I D
```

WORD BOX

animals	eden	man
beautiful	fruit	tree
creation	garden	woman
disobeyed	loved	world

Two Brothers

Genesis 4:1-16

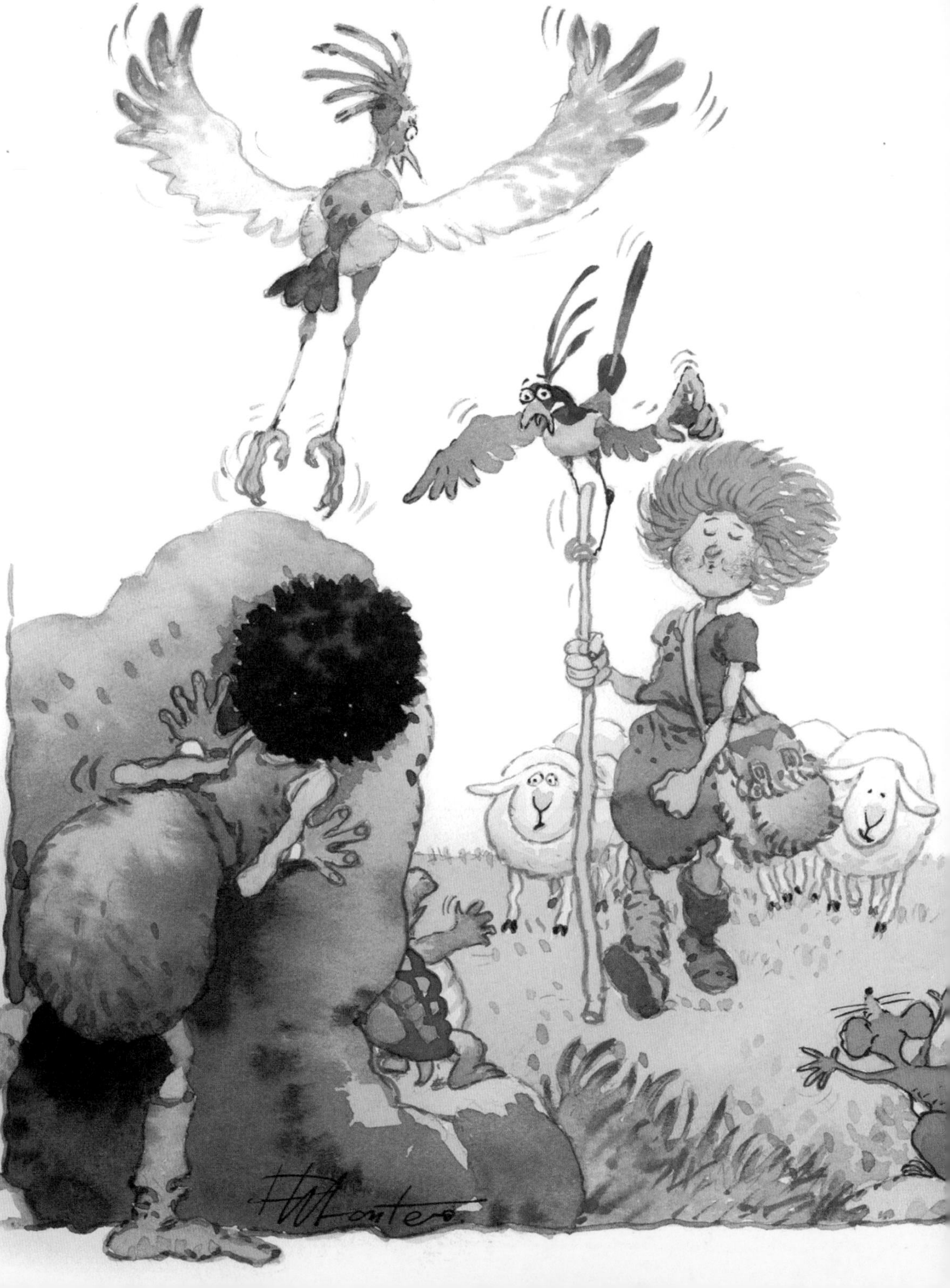

Adam and Eve had made a home for themselves outside the garden. It was not long before God blessed them with children. They had one son named Cain and a second son named Abel.

Cain and Abel each had a special job. Cain was the farmer. He made sure all the crops grew nice and tall. His younger brother was the shepherd. Abel made sure that all the animals were taken care of.

Adam and Eve had taught their children to give God thanks. All good things, after all, came from God. So, they gave God back a bit of the good things He had given to them. Cain offered God some of his crop. Abel offered some of his flock.

God likes Abel's gift more, Cain thought. Cain felt jealous. The feeling grew and grew until Cain decided to get rid of Abel. Cain killed his brother and then tried to hide the truth.

Yet nothing is a secret from God. Cain would have to pay for what he had done. God sent Cain to wander the world alone. Even still, God promised to keep Cain safe.

"Anyone who hurts you," God promised Cain,
"I will punish them seven times worse."
God would even bless Cain with a family one day.

FIND THE LAMB

Help Abel find the lamb to offer to God. On the way, collect the letters and write them down in order to find out the word that means "to give your best."

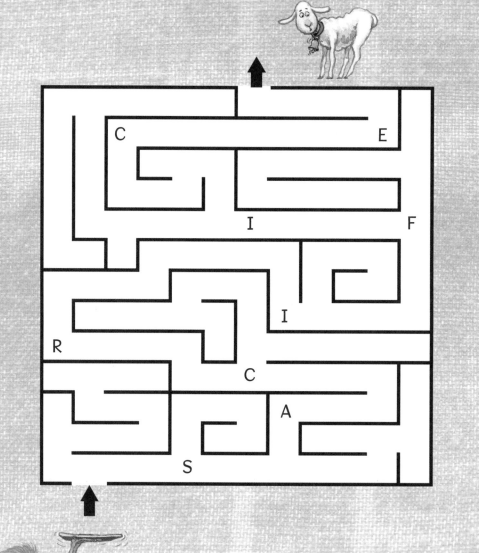

The word is:

_____

ABEL THE SHEPHERD

Abel wanted to give his very best to God, so Abel gave the first lamb of his flock. How many times can you find the word LAMB in this grid? It can be up, down, across, backwards, and diagonally.

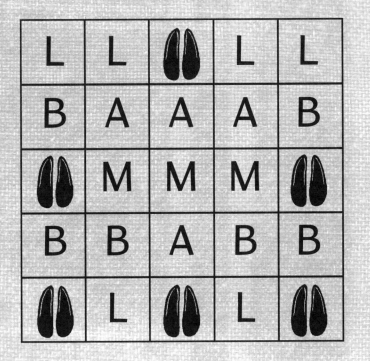

The word "lamb" can be found _____ times.

The Good Shepherd

God is like a good shepherd. He knows us, leads us, protects us, and keeps us from harm.

God Calls on Noah

Genesis 6:5-22

The world had turned rotten. Here and there, the people turned to sin. Was there any person left who would listen to God?

Noah was just the one for the job. Noah loved God more than anything on Earth. And whatever God told Him, Noah would do. "I want you to build a big boat," God told Noah, "because I am starting the world again fresh."

The boat was built in just the way God wanted. Then Noah and his family collected the animals. Onto the boat they went, two by two . . . those that slithered and those that creeped, those that flew and those that hopped. There was room for every sort, each in its place.

"Take aboard every animal," said God to Noah, "those that fly and creep and walk. Keep them alive for the new world to come."

DRAW A BIRD

Noah gathered up all the animals including birds. Use the grid to help you draw one of the birds, square by square. Then you can color it.

ANIMAL CROSSWORD

Complete the puzzle with the names of the animals listed below.

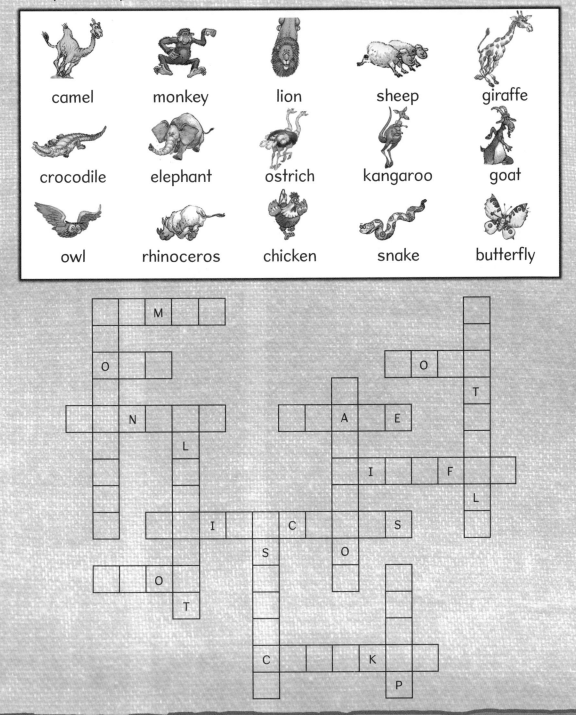

camel   monkey   lion   sheep   giraffe

crocodile   elephant   ostrich   kangaroo   goat

owl   rhinoceros   chicken   snake   butterfly

The Great Flood
Genesis 7:17-24; 8:1-19

Drip, drip, drip. The last of the animals had been loaded aboard when it began to rain. Noah's family went inside. God shut the heavy ark door tightly with a loud boom.

It rained and it rained for forty days straight. It rained until the whole Earth was covered. At last the rain stopped. They peeked outside. There was nothing to see except water. The ark was floating in an endless sea.

Noah sent a dove to look for dry land. The dove came back once. It came back twice. But the third time . . . what was that in it's beak? A twig of green—the Earth was getting dry! When the dove came back no more, Noah knew it had found a home. And that very soon, the rest of them would as well.

BOATS

Noah built an ark, which is a very large boat. Find 2 compound words ending in the word BOAT. The picture is there to help you.

_ _ _ _ BOAT

_ _ _ BOAT

How many boats can you find in the drawing below? _____

MAZE

The dove left the ark in search of land. Help the dove find the tree.

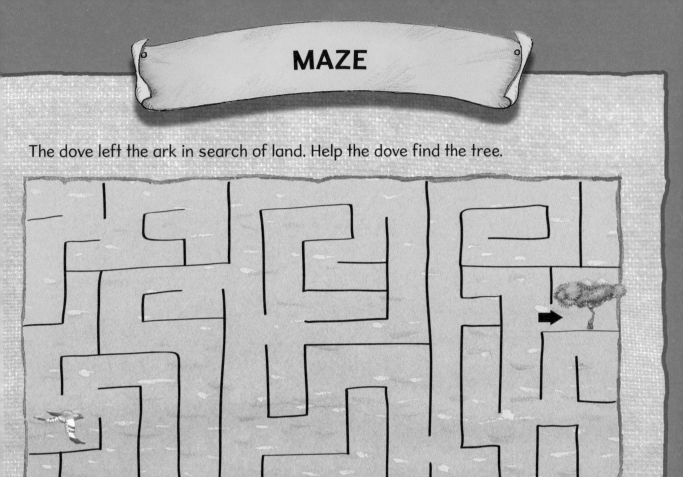

STORY QUIZ

Did you listen carefully to the story? Try to answer the following questions:

1. How many days did it rain?

_____

2. What bird did Noah send out to look for dry land?

_____

Promise in a Rainbow
Genesis 9:1-17

What a feeling to be back on land! The animals went leaping and tumbling into the sweet grass of spring.

God had done all He had promised. He had kept all aboard safe and sound. He had given them a world, fresh and new.

Noah built an altar and got down on his knees. How great God was! How much He must love them! Noah gave God thanks and sang Him praises. On the altar, Noah laid sweet gifts for God.

God gave a gift as well. There above them gleamed ribbons of color . . . red and yellow, green and blue. This was the very first rainbow. God gave it as a promise that He would never flood the whole Earth again.

God said, "The rainbow is a sign to be seen through all of time to remind us all that never again will water destroy the Earth."

WORD SEARCH

Find the 14 hidden words taken from the story of God's promise for Noah.
They can be found up, down, across, backwards, and diagonally.

```
L U H E U F U N E X G P
H I S R D F L E R S N R
E M E U S E O O E M I A
H J R T B E M L O Y R I
A G F A R L S A Y D P S
L R N E I I L N T T S E
T S T R N N L D K U T S
A I H G M G B Y D I A O
R G J I F T N O B B I R
Q N W F I E P G W S F O
P U T T W E V O O S I X
R A M Q D W S C O L O R
P R O M I S E E H B O T
```

WORD BOX

altar	gift	ribbon
color	land	sign
feeling	praises	spring
flood	promise	sweet
fresh	rainbow	

WHAT IS DIFFERENT?

Can you find 10 differences between each set of pictures?

The Tower of Babel

Genesis 10:32-11:9

People built up towns. The towns turned into cities. Soon people got to thinking they were mightier than God. "Why wait on God?" said one neighbor to another. "We could build a tower to Heaven and climb there ourselves."

The plan was set in motion. Brick by brick, the tower rose high.

God saw everything. And easier than they could build it, God could bring it down.

God decided to bring down their egos instead. All of a sudden, every builder spoke a different language. Each thought it was the other who was speaking gibberish. No one could understand one another. No one could cooperate. "It's all this tower's fault," they said. "Whose idea was it anyway?"

"You were so proud," says God, "that you got yourself tricked.
You built your place up high like you were some mighty eagle.
You said to yourself, 'Who can bring me down?'
I will bring you down," says God, "for all your wicked deeds."

THE TOWER

Follow the line for each letter to find out where the letter goes.

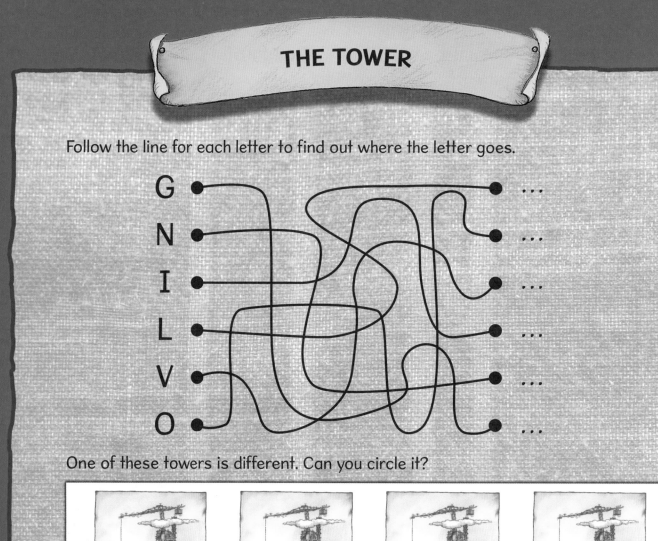

G ● ...
N ● ...
I ● ...
L ● ...
V ● ...
O ● ...

One of these towers is different. Can you circle it?

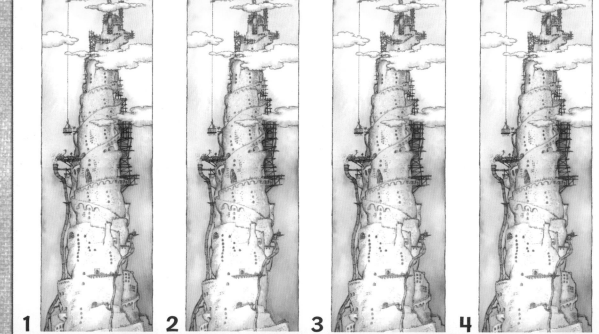

1   2   3   4

LANGUAGES & COUNTRIES

God punished the people of Babel by giving them each their own language.
Today, people live in many different countries speaking their own languages.

Where are you from? Can you find your country on the map?

Can you also find on the map:
1. the boy with blond hair wearing the white and red sweater
2. the Mexican boy with a hat and a striped scarf
3. the Japanese lady with an umbrella
4. the Aboriginal Australian boy holding a spear

Abraham & Sarah

Genesis 12-13, 17

"Yes," said Abraham and Sarah. They would go anywhere that God told them to go. No journey would be too long if it was God's plan.

They would even sleep in a tent. They would camp out in the desert as long as God wanted. When things felt less than comfy, they just hung in there. They knew that God was always planning good things for the faithful.

What they did not know was that God's plan was better than they could dream up. He had sent them away to bring them home, to build a new nation . . . that would all begin with them.

"Look up at the sky," God told Abraham. "Do you see all the stars above?" asked God. "Your family will one day be as many as the stars, as many as the grains of sand on the seashore."

A LONG JOURNEY

Can you find and circle these things in the picture?

1. a dog
2. a grey goat
3. a mouse wearing pants

4. a suitcase with a flower
5. a frying pan
6. a red bell

DID YOU KNOW?

Abraham (Abram) is a descendant of Shem, son of Noah. Noah was still alive when Abraham was born.

A NOMAD'S LIFE

Help Abraham find the oasis in the desert. You need to avoid the dangers on the way!

Synonyms are words that have the same meaning. Draw a line to connect the synonyms together.

LAND	CAMP
BIVOUAC	WASTELAND
PROMISE	COMMITMENT
TRUST	REGION
DESERT	FAITH

Abraham's Great Big Family

Genesis 15, 17:1-16, 18:1-15, 21:1-8

What God had promised, God would do. And He had promised a great big family to Sarah and Abraham. Sometimes the two doubted and worried when they had no child. But God always had a plan.

They waited. And waited. They waited so long that their hair turned gray.

One day, some angels in disguise came by. The visitors said that Abraham and Sarah would soon have a child.

Sarah laughed right out loud. Who ever heard of two old folks having a baby?! Yet sure enough, it happened. Baby Isaac was the start of a great big family for Abraham and Sarah.

"Lift up your eyes," God said to Abraham. "Look north, and look south. Look east, and look west. All the land that you see, I will fill with your people."

From Abraham to Jacob

ABRAHAM

SARAH

ISAAC

REBEKAH

JACOB

Each description is about someone from Abraham's closest family. Read the descriptions carefully and write down to whom they belong.

_ _ _ _ _

was the wife of Abraham and the mother of Isaac. Her name was originally Sarai. The new name God gave her means "princess."

_ _ _ _ _

was the only son Abraham and Sarah had, and he was the father of Jacob and Esau.

_ _ _ _ _

He was the son of Isaac and Rebekah. He had 13 children: 12 sons and one daughter. One of them was Joseph, who later became ruler of Egypt.

_ _ _ _ _ _ _

means "father of many nations." At first his name was Abram (father is exalted), but God changed it.

THE VISITORS

Can you find 10 differences between these two pictures?

A Coat of Many Colors
Genesis 37

It was a lovely coat indeed. And it proved what the brothers had always feared - that their father loved Joseph the most. Joseph was their kid brother who bragged about dreams of the future and said they would one day bow down to him.

Time for Joseph to learn his lesson, the brothers decided. So they sold him to a group of traders who were heading to a land far away.

Joseph was now captured as a slave. Even still, he did not give up believing. Joseph was sure that God would save him.

And that's just what God did. Joseph was made servant to a rich man, a man who knew a good heart when he saw one. He soon put Joseph in charge of his whole estate. Joseph had always believed that staying true to God no matter what is the best thing to do.

Color Joseph's coat of many colors.
You can also draw a pattern on it.

Unscramble a Bible verse from Joseph's story using the code below.

✿ = A	✛ = K	▼ = U
■ = B	⊖ = L	◇ = V
❖ = C	□ = M	⊘ = W
✳ = D	✳ = N	? = X
✌ = E	● = O	☀ = Y
◉ = F	❄ = P	△ = Z
▲ = G	◆ = Q	
❄ = H	✳ = R	
○ = I	✕ = S	
⃝ = J	◻ = T	

Decoded verse:

WHEN JOSEPH

CAME TO HIS

BROTHERS, THEY

PULLED OFF THE

FANCY COAT.

Genesis 37:23 CEV

50

SOLD BY HIS BROTHERS

Use the clues to solve the crossword puzzle about Joseph's story.

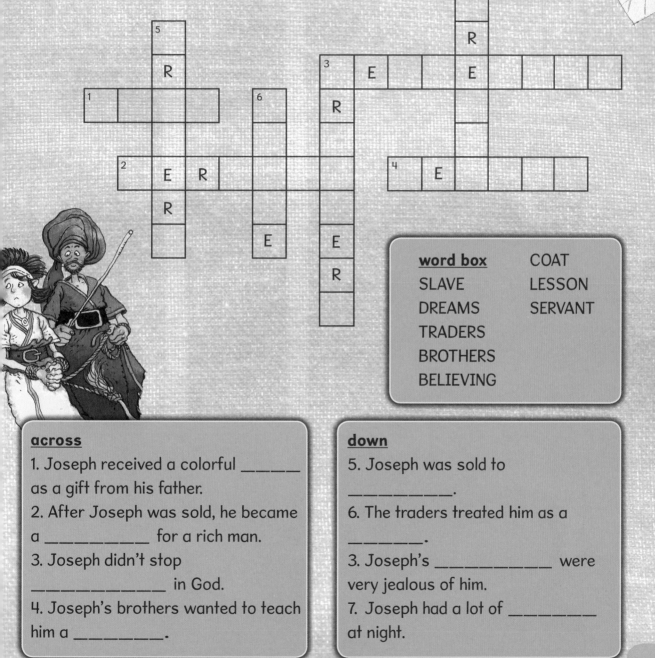

word box

COAT
SLAVE   LESSON
DREAMS   SERVANT
TRADERS
BROTHERS
BELIEVING

across

1. Joseph received a colorful _____ as a gift from his father.
2. After Joseph was sold, he became a _____ for a rich man.
3. Joseph didn't stop _____ in God.
4. Joseph's brothers wanted to teach him a _____.

down

5. Joseph was sold to _____.
6. The traders treated him as a _____.
3. Joseph's _____ were very jealous of him.
7. Joseph had a lot of _____ at night.

The Faith of Joseph

Genesis 39-46

Things had just started going well for Joseph. But someone got jealous. They told a lie, and Joseph was thrown in jail. Yet like before, Joseph knew God would save him. So he did not sit in a corner sad and glum. Joseph helped the other prisoners instead.

One day, the king had a dream. No one knew what it meant. Just then, the cupbearer spoke up. He had met a man in the jail who knew about dreams.

Joseph was brought out. "Your dream means that a famine is coming," said Joseph bravely, "so you must start saving food." The king was so grateful that he put his ring on Joseph's finger. He dressed Joseph like a king. Then he made Joseph second-in-command over all the land. Surely God was with Joseph; the king realized it well.

That would have been a fine ending. Yet with God, there is always more good in store. One day his brothers came looking for food. Would the mighty ruler spare them a wee bit of corn?

Joseph was overjoyed to see his family. "It's me, Joseph!" he cried. Joseph forgave his brothers for selling him away. Then they all got to come live with Joseph in the land of plenty.

JOSEPH OUT OF PRISON

Which path did Joseph take from the prison to go see the pharaoh?

Look at Joseph carefully. Which shadow is his?

1   2   3   4

Write the next letter that comes in each pattern below and find out what is the name of Joseph's younger brother.

H - I - B - H - I - B - H - I - B - H - I - (B)

R - R - T - E - R - R - T - E - R - R - T - (E)

O - T - O - T - N - O - T - O - T - (N)

A - I - R - U - J - A - I - R - U - (J)

M - S - R - R - A - M - S - R - R - (A)

P - E - P - M - P - E - P - (M)

D - G - U - I - I - D - G - U - I - (I)

Z - K - L - N - Z - K - L - N - Z - K - L - (N)

The name is: __ __ __ __ __ __ __ __.

The Baby in a Basket
Exodus 2:1-10

A new king was in charge, a king so awful that no one but his family was safe.

Miriam loved her baby brother. She wanted to help keep him safe. So, Miriam did just as her mother told her. She put baby Moses into a basket. Then, Miriam floated the basket in the river. She watched from the reeds nearby to see what would happen.

The plan could not have worked out better! The royal princess came along to take her bath. Just then, her eye caught sight of something strange. "Look!" she cried out to her servants. "It's a baby in a basket."

The princess scooped Moses into her arms.
"I think I will adopt him," said the princess.

God was watching over them every minute.
God had a special job for Moses to do one day.
"I will be with you," God would tell him.
"I will teach you what to say and what to do."

A MEAN PHARAOH

The new pharaoh was afraid of the Hebrews, so he made them slaves. The Hebrews worked to build everything. Look at the picture below. Can you find:

1. 13 men working for pharaoh
2. 11 baskets

DID YOU KNOW

The pharoah was so afraid that he decided the male children of the Israelites should be killed. Moses was one of them. So Moses' mother placed him in a basket and sent her 12-year-old daughter, Miriam, to watch where the basket floated.

The daughter of the pharaoh found the baby in the basket and named him Moses, which means "drawn out," because he was drawn out of the water.

BABY MOSES

Find the 12 hidden words taken from the story of baby Moses. They can be found up, down, across, backwards, and diagonally.

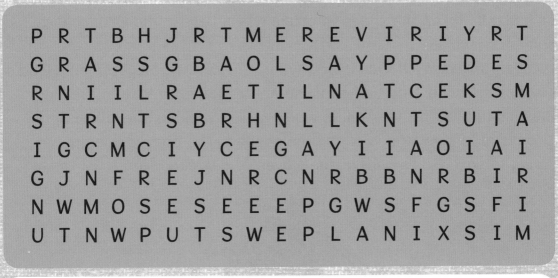

```
P R T B H J R T M E R E V I R I Y R T
G R A S S G B A O L S A Y P P E D E S
R N I I L R A E T I L N A T C E K S M
S T R N T S B R H N L L K N T S U T A
I G C M C I Y C E G A Y I I A O I A I
G J N F R E J N R C N R B B N R B I R
N W M O S E S E E P G W S F G S F I
U T N W P U T S W E P L A N I X S I M
```

WORD BOX

baby	king	mother	prince
basket	Miriam	palace	princess
grass	Moses	plan	river

Which one of the babies in the basket is different? Circle it.

2   3   4

59

The Burning Bush

Exodus 1-4

Moses was a prince, but enough was enough. The king was simply too cruel for Moses to stick around. And so, he ran away. Moses found a new family, and life was finally starting to feel normal.

That's when it happened. A bush exploded into fire right in front of him. Moses had only taken the sheep to graze when, here in the wilderness, God had come for him.

Moses felt afraid. What was it God wanted? "Return to Egypt," said God's voice out of the bush. God had a message for Moses to take to the king.

Moses did not feel brave. And he was awful at making speeches. But God promised to give Moses all that he needed if he obeyed. Moses was going to save God's people, the slaves of a wicked king.

"Go where I have sent you," said God, "and I will teach you what to say."

Find out more about what happened to Moses after he ran away. Change each bold letter to the next letter in the alphabet.

Moses ran to hide in a region called

LHCHZM. There he married a woman named

....

Zipporah and became a **RGDOGDQC**, and

....

took care of many **ZMHLZKR**.

....

DID YOU KNOW?
Moses stuttered and stammered. That is why when God told him to free the Israelites from slavery, he was afraid. But God had a plan.

MOSES' CALLING

Find the 10 differences between the two pictures.

Find the names of four members of Moses' family: Miriam, Aaron, Jethro and Zipporah. Cross out one letter at a time to complete the names. You can go up, down, left, or right, but each letter can only be used once.

M	I	A	M	A
Z	R	I	R	A
I	P	P	O	N
A	R	O	H	R
H	J	E	T	O

Journey Through the Sea
Exodus 5-16

Moses stood in front of the king. "Let God's people *go*," said Moses. The king just laughed. Instead of letting slaves go, he would now work them even harder.

So God turned the water to blood. Then frogs came out of the river and covered everything. The whole land soon got lice, and clouds of flies filled up the palace. Everyone got sick. There was thunder and hail, then giant bugs. Then, every firstborn died, even the cows. At long last, the king had enough. "Get out of here," he told Moses. And take those slaves and those curses with you!

The people of God packed their things. Then they fled away with Moses to guide them. He knew where to go by the pillars of smoke and fire God put in the sky.

But there was a problem - a big problem. They had run into the sea! And even worse, it looked like the king had changed his mind because here he came with his army chasing after them. Had God led them to the sea just to get caught . . . or *drown*?

Moses reached out his staff, and God split apart the sea. Huge towers of waves pealed back. A path lay in between. The people ran across as quickly as they could. Safe on the other side, Moses reached out again. The waves closed up just like they'd been before. All the king's army that chased them was washed away.

OUT OF EGYPT

Unscramble the words taken from Moses' story.

SORGF

POLEPE

SVELAS

OKSME

FATSF

YRAM

BERLPOM

VEWAS

word box

ARMY	SLAVES
FROGS	SMOKE
PEOPLE	STAFF
PROBLEM	WAVES

across

1. God put pillars of _____ in the sky to show the way.
2. What Moses and the Hebrew people faced when they arrived to the sea.
3. Washed away the king's army.
4. The king treated Moses' people as _____.

down

5. Because the king didn't listen, _____ rained from the sky.
6. Moses asked the king to let his _____ go.
7. What Moses was holding in front of the sea.
8. The king's _____ was chasing Moses and his people.

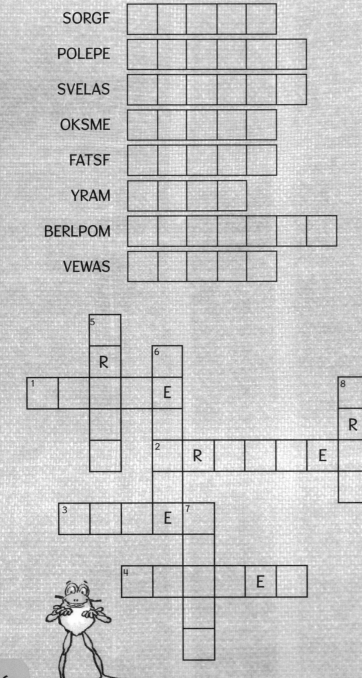

CROSSING THE SEA

Find the close-ups
in the picture.

1

2

3

4

5

God told Joshua, "I will never fail you. I will never leave you. All you need to do is be strong and be brave."

God said to Joshua, "Be strong, and be brave." It was time to leave the desert. It was time to cross the Jordan. God would be with the people in every step. Joshua got the people together. Then, across the river they went. And what a lovely sight on the other side! No more sand, but a land green and lush. This was the land God had promised . . . a land of milk and honey. A land that would be their own.

There was just one problem. Jericho was a city with high, stone walls. How were they ever going to beat a city like *that*?

God told Joshua just what to do. They would not use weapons—but trumpets.

Joshua knew better than to disobey God however silly a plan might seem. He marched the people around the city just like God had said. Around, and around, and around. After seven times, everyone gave a great shout. The priests all blew their trumpets. And in one mighty quake, Jericho toppled to the ground!

BECOMING A LEADER

Use the code below to find out what God said to Joshua when he became a leader.

A=1
B=2
C=3
D=4
E=5
F=6
G=7
H=8
I=9
J=10
K=11
L=12
M=13
N=14
O=15
P=16
Q=17
R=18
S=19
T=20
U=21
V=22
W=23
X=24
Y=25
Z=26

9 22 5   3 15 13 13 1 14 4 5 4
◯'◯◯ ◯ ◯ ◯ ◯ ◯ ◯ ◯ ◯ ◯

25 15 21   20 15   2 5
◯ ◯ ◯ ◯ ◯ ◯ ◯

19 20 18 15 14 7   1 14 4
◯ ◯ ◯ ◯ ◯ ◯ ◯ ◯ ◯

2 18 1 22 5
◯ ◯ ◯ ◯ ◯.

Joshua 1:9 CEV

70

Did you listen to the story carefully? Write the numbers 1-4 to put the story in order.

Gideon Wants Proof
Judges 6-7

Gideon had a hard time believing it. Did God really choose a farmer to be a warrior? Surely there was someone better. After all, the enemy was ferocious.

So Gideon had to pray to find his faith. "If You truly want me to fight," said Gideon, "then show me a sign, God. Make this wool wet while the ground stays dry." The next morning the wool was wet. The ground was dry.

Gideon prayed again. The enemy was *so* scary that Gideon needed to be extra sure God would be there. He hoped God would not be mad, but . . . would God now do the opposite? The next morning, the ground was wet. The wool was dry.

Gideon was still small and still poor. But he now had all he needed. He had faith in God. So Gideon stormed into battle with God by his side. One hand held a trumpet. One hand held a torch. The land was saved from it's enemy by only a farmer.

"Still too many soldiers," God said to Gideon. God wanted Gideon to have the smallest army possible. That way, all would know who had won the fight. God had won it with Gideon as His servant.

THE SMALL ARMY

Look at the pictures carefully, and find in each row the one that is different.

DID YOU KNOW?
After Gideon defeated the Midianites, he was a judge over Israel for 40 years.

THE BATTLE

Find the 10 differences between the two pictures.

Samson the Strong

Judges 13-14, 16

He was only a kid when he once killed a lion and with only his bare hands at that. He was stronger than strong, tougher than tough. No one could beat Samson.

His enemies would still try, of course. If only they knew his secret. *What made Samson so strong?* they wondered. *And what was it that would take it all away?*

When a spy learned the truth, it seemed all too easy. God had ordered Samson to never cut his hair. So while Samson slept—*snip, snip*. They tied him with rope. Samson usually snapped ropes without trying. But this time, it no longer worked. Samson was captured. But little did anyone realize . . .

In jail, Samson's hair just grew and grew. One day, the enemy wanted some fun. Samson was brought out. They tied him to pillars. "Look at silly Samson," they laughed.

"Please God," Samson prayed, "give me strength just one last time." Samson put his hands on the pillars. He pushed with all his might. The whole building toppled, and all of his enemies went with it.

STRONGER THAN STRONG

Join the dots and find the animal Samson killed with his bare hands.

DID YOU KNOW?

Samson's mother couldn't have babies. God sent a messenger to tell her that she would have a very special son who would help deliver Israel.

Samson, meaning sunshine, was born during a dark period of Israel's history. At that time, the Israelites had turned from God and were under the oppression of the Philistines.

SAMSON'S STRENGTH

Samson had great strengh which was given by God. Other words can be used to describe strength. In each box below, draw a line to make words with a similar meaning.

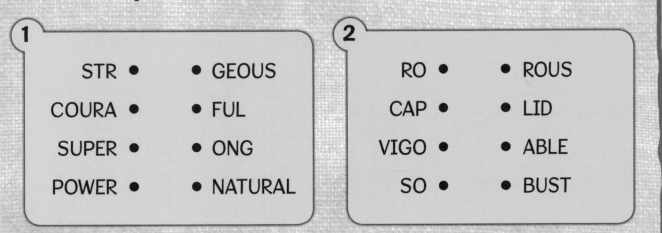

1

STR •   • GEOUS

COURA •   • FUL

SUPER •   • ONG

POWER •   • NATURAL

2

RO •   • ROUS

CAP •   • LID

VIGO •   • ABLE

SO •   • BUST

Think through your strengths—the unique gifts, talents, and abilities God has given you. Write them down.

_____

_____

_____

_____

_____

_____

_____

Ruth's Reward

Ruth 1-4

Ruth would not budge. Her husband had died, and her mother-in-law was letting Ruth go home. That meant Ruth could be with her old friends again. She could see her parents and get taken care of again.

Yet Ruth knew what was wrong and what was right. And she was not leaving this poor older woman to travel alone. "Where you go, I will go," Ruth said to Naomi. "Your people will be my people. Your God will be my God." What could Naomi do but agree?

Ruth worked hard to help Naomi. All day long, Ruth gathered grain for their food. Naomi wished she could pay Ruth back for all her kindness.

Naomi had an idea. Did she not have a relative named Boaz with plenty to share? Ruth had already met him. It was his field where Ruth found her grain. And what better gift for Ruth than a new chance at love.

Ruth paid a visit to Boaz. She did just as Naomi had told her. And now, Boaz had a question for Ruth . . . would she be his wife? Soon they were married, and Naomi became a grandma at last.

"I know the plans I have for you," says God. "They are plans for good and not for hurt. They are plans to give you a future and a hope. Then at last you will come to Me. You will pray, and I will listen. You will find Me when you search with all your heart."

Ruth and Naomi went to Bethlehem. Which path did they take?

DID YOU KNOW?

Ruth is King David's great grand-mother, and she is also the ancestor of Joseph, husband of Mary and father to Jesus.

LOYALTY

Unscramble an important verse from Ruth's story using the code below.

A=1
B=2
C=3
D=4
E=5
F=6
G=7
H=8
I=9
J=10
K=11
L=12
M=13
N=14
O=15
P=16
Q=17
R=18
S=19
T=20
U=21
V=22
W=23
X=24
Y=25
Z=26

25 15 21 18　　16 5 15 16 12 5
Y O U R 　　 P E O P L E

23 9 12 12　　2 5　　13 25
W I L L 　　B E 　 M Y

16 5 15 16 12 5 ,　　25 15 21 18
P E O P L E 　　　Y O U R

7 15 4　　23 9 12 12　　2 5
G O D 　　W I L L 　　B E

13 25　　7 15 4 .
M Y 　　G O D

Ruth 1:16 CEV

83

The Shepherd Boy

1 Samuel 16

Jesse was thrilled to have the prophet Samuel in his very own home! And even more thrilled that Samuel brought wonderful news. God had chosen one of Jesse's own sons . . . to be *king!*

Jesse lined up his big, strong sons. Samuel looked over each one blankly. And now Jesse was getting worried; maybe Samuel had come to the wrong house after all. Samuel said at last, "Are these *all* your sons?"

Jesse gave a pause. Samuel could not mean—"Well, no," said Jesse, "there's the youngest out watching the sheep. But David is only a *boy!*"

Samuel seemed interested, so Jesse called David inside. As soon as

Samuel set eyes on him, his face beamed. "*That's* the one!" said Samuel. God had picked the smallest to be a king. Because to God it's the size of the heart that matters most. Right then and there, Samuel anointed David . . . their future king.

"You, oh God!" sang David, "are my strength and my shield. From You alone, oh God, will I take commands."

What did David fight to protect the sheep? Color the areas with dots to find out.

Can you find which shadow matches the shape you colored?

PLAYING THE HARP

David liked to play the harp and sing. Find 12 other names of musical instruments below. They can be found up, down, across, backwards, and diagonally.

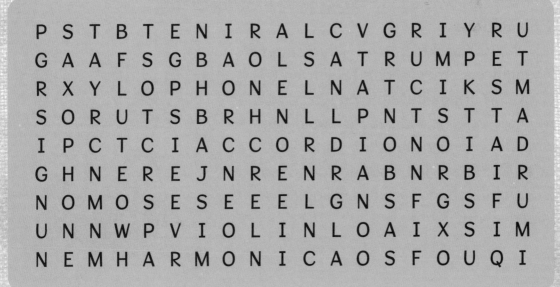

```
P S T B T E N I R A L C V G R I Y R U
G A A F S G B A O L S A T R U M P E T
R X Y L O P H O N E L N A T C I K S M
S O R U T S B R H N L L P N T S T T A
I P C T C I A C C O R D I O N O I A D
G H N E R E J N R E N R A B N R B I R
N O M O S E S E E E L G N S F G S F U
U N N W P V I O L I N L O A I X S I M
N E M H A R M O N I C A O S F O U Q I
```

WORD BOX

accordion	drum	harmonica	trumpet
cello	flute	piano	violin
clarinet	guitar	saxophone	xylophone

David & Goliath

1 Samuel 17

The earth shook with the giant's every step. "Grrr-AR!" Goliath growled. The soldiers all hid behind their shields.

"I will fight him," said a squeaky voice. David's brothers looked up from their hiding places. Was their kid brother trying to get himself *killed*? He was supposed to bring them lunch then scurry home again.

David was not backing down. *What could it hurt?* thought the army leader. They tried to dress David in armor, but nothing would fit a boy. So David said no thanks. He would beat the giant with only his slingshot—and God.

Whoosh. David whirled his sling round and round. Goliath stepped forward swinging a giant-sized sword.

"You come with a sword," yelled David, "but I come in the name of God!" Then, David let loose. His rock went zooming through the air. *Crack!*—the mighty giant toppled. And so the battle was won by just a boy.

"Praise God, you His angels," sang David. "Praise Him, sun and moon. Praise Him, all you stars of light. Praise Him, heavens and waters. Let all things praise the name of God . . . for it's God who has made all things."

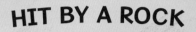

Color Goliath being hit by the rock.

A GIANT AND A BOY

Find the 10 differences between the two pictures.

The Wisest King
2 Samuel 12; 1 Kings 3; 2 Chronicles 1

King David had been loved by all. So that when
he died, the sadness seemed like it would never
ever end.

Yet God is full of surprises. And next in line
was the most famous king of all time: King
Solomon the wise, David's very own son.

It had all come about in a dream when
Solomon was just a young man. God had
given him one wish. Instead of riches or
fame, Solomon asked to be wise. God was
so pleased that He gave Solomon a bonus.
Not only would Solomon be wise, but he
would have riches and fame as well.

It did not take long at all for his
people to understand that this was a
mighty king indeed. Building a house for
God? Solomon was the one to make
it happen. Judging right and wrong?
Solomon found a way.

One day, two mothers came to him.
"This is my baby," said one. "No, it's
mine," said the other. Yet Solomon had
a plan. How about if they shared the
baby?

One of the women cried out, "Surely
the child would be better with only one
mother. Let her take the baby."

The woman had thought about the child
more than herself. Now King Solomon knew
just who the real mother was.

"If you seek," said Solomon, "and if you ask for understanding, if you look for it like silver or hidden treasure, then you will understand the truth that comes from God. For it's God who gives all wisdom and all knowledge."

BUILDING A TEMPLE

Can you find:

1. a dog chasing a cat
2. a man carving the wall
3. a woman serving a drink
4. four hammers

SOLOMON'S WISDOM

Which shadow belongs to the man holding the baby?

1   2   3   4

Find out some facts about God's temple by changing all the bold letters with the letter that comes before it in the alphabet.

In the **GPVSUI** year of his reign, Solomon began

....

the **DPOTUSVDUJPO** of the Temple. **TFWFO**

....

years later it was completed, and the **BSL** of the

....

DPWFOBOU was moved to the Temple.

....

95

Elijah the Prophet

1 Kings 16-17, 19; 2 Kings 2

The meanest of kings was no match for a prophet. Elijah would deliver any message God told him. Even if it put him in danger so that he had to hide out. In the woods or in the desert, God was always taking care.

The king was getting punished just like Elijah had warned. There was a famine in the land. Elijah's belly rumbled. God told him to go into town.

The woman at the town gate was gathering firewood when she heard the man's voice. He wanted a bit of bread. "Sir," said the woman, "I have barely enough for me and my son!" Little did she know, she was speaking to a prophet.

Elijah told the woman she would never run out if she helped him. As she poured the last of her flour and oil—sure enough, the jars could not be emptied out!

"Leave from here," God told Elijah, who had the evil king on his tail. "Go east, and hide by a brook. You will drink from this brook, and I will send ravens to feed you." Elijah obeyed. The ravens dropped bread and meat from their beaks for him both morning and night.

ELIJAH THE PROPHET

Unscramble the words taken from the story of Elijah and use the clues to solve the crossword puzzle.

ERDAB

MAFIEN

SAVREN

ORBOK

SEGEMAS

NAWOM

THORPPE

RULFO

word box

PROPHET	FLOUR
MESSAGE	BROOK
FAMINE	RAVENS
WOMAN	BREAD

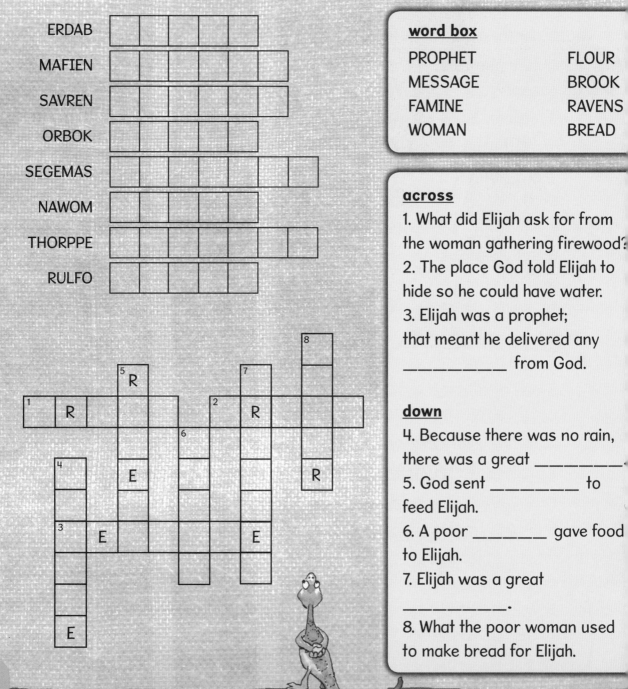

across

1. What did Elijah ask for from the woman gathering firewood?
2. The place God told Elijah to hide so he could have water.
3. Elijah was a prophet; that meant he delivered any _____ from God.

down

4. Because there was no rain, there was a great _____
5. God sent _____ to feed Elijah.
6. A poor _____ gave food to Elijah.
7. Elijah was a great _____.
8. What the poor woman used to make bread for Elijah.

ELIJAH AND THE RAVENS

Which way did the ravens take to bring food to Elijah?

FACTS ABOUT RAVENS

Ravens are cousins with the crows but have a greater size and a larger and heavier black beak. They are unusually intelligent. Like other corvids, Ravens can mimic sounds from their environment, including human speech.

Esther, Brave & Fair
Esther 2-10

Who was the fairest in all the land? When the king met Esther, the rest were history. Esther was all that a queen should be . . . she was good and beautiful and wise.

Esther was one more thing. She was a stranger in the land. The king didn't know that when he agreed to let Esther's people be killed!

Esther had a hard choice. The truth might finish her, then and there.

Yet keeping her secret would have felt worse, much, much worse. So Esther got dressed in her finest gown. She dressed her heart in bravery.

"My queen!" said the king when he saw his love. Was there anything she wanted? Esther took a deep breath. There was just one thing she wanted, Esther told the king. Would the king let Esther and her people *live?* The king was furious that anyone would *dare* want to kill his wonderful bride! The plan had worked. Brave Queen Esther had saved her people. The king sent out a new order to stop Esther's people, God's people, from being killed.

In every state and in every city, everywhere the new order came, and Esther's people had joy and gladness, a feast, and a mighty good day!

ESTHER THE QUEEN

How many overlapping crowns can you find here?

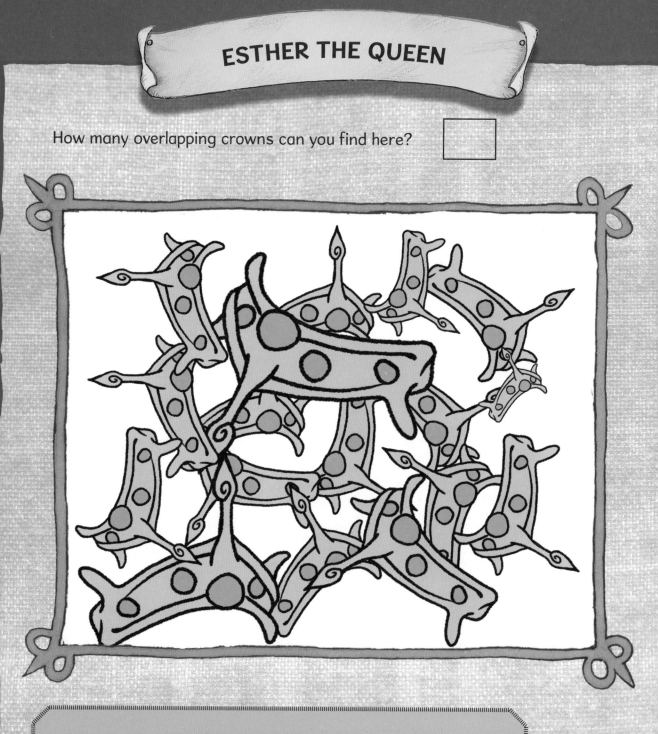

DID YOU KNOW?

Esther means star. Esther's parents died when she was a young girl, and she was raised by her uncle.

ESTHER'S UNCLE

Write the next letter that comes in the pattern and find out the name of Esther's uncle.

Y - U - M - Y - U - M - Y - U - M - Y - U - (__)

A - A - L - O - A - A - L - O - A - A - L - (__)

W - T - W - T - R - W - T - W - T - (__)

E - I - M - U - D - E - I - M - U - (__)

F - F - R - E - F - F - R - E - F - F - R - (__)

A - C - P - I - A - C - P - I - A - (__)

D - G - U - O - A - D - G - U - O - (__)

Q - U - L - I - Q - U - L - I - Q - U - L - (__)

His name is: __ __ __ __ __ __ __ __ .

The Lion's Den

2 Kings 25; 2 Chronicles 36; Jeremiah 39-40, 52; Daniel 1

How had God's servant ended up among lions? He had done everything right, after all. Daniel had obeyed God, through and through. He had served the king of the land with honor and truth.

It was a case as old as time. Daniel had done so well that others got jealous. Some rulers thought, *why should Daniel get power?* The jealous ones tricked the king into getting rid of Daniel.

Daniel's enemies had not counted on how mighty God really was. In the darkness of the pit, Daniel prayed. Daniel believed that God would save him as He always had before.

"I give thanks to God of Heaven," prayed Daniel, "to Him who uncovers things kept deep and secret. God knows all things that lie out in the darkness. And with God is where there is light."

The king was sick with worry. It was morning, and he ran to the pit of lions. Had Daniel's God been able to save him even from ferocious lions?

"I'm okay!" Daniel called up. "God has saved me," he said to the king's relief. God had sent an angel to shut the lions' mouths.

DANIEL'S STORY

Did you listen to the story carefully? Write 1 through 4 to put the story in order.

DID YOU KNOW?

When the Babylonians conquered Israel, they took many young men into captivity in Babylon. One of them was Daniel. When Daniel was thrown into the lions' den, he was in his 80s.

IN THE LIONS' DEN

Find the 10 differences between the two pictures.

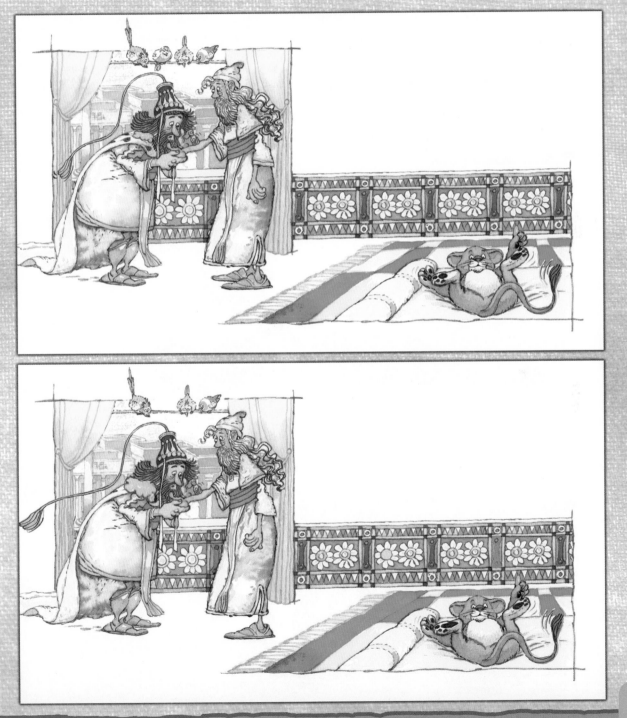

Jonah & the Whale

Jonah 1-4

Go and tell a city that God was angry? "No thank you," said Jonah. God's plan did not sound like much fun at all.

So Jonah ran away. He got on a ship for a distant land. Who could find him now? Jonah was free and clear, he thought.

Jonah was dead wrong. God knew exactly where Jonah was the whole time. And when that ship started shaking, Jonah knew why. "This storm will swallow us alive!" cried one sailor. It was time for Jonah to tell the truth: that God sent the storm because Jonah had not obeyed. So throw Jonah over, and the ship would be saved.

Jonah bobbed in the sea, afraid and alone. But God is forgiving. And God had a plan. A giant fish swallowed Jonah up in one big *gulp!*

Inside the fish, Jonah had plenty of time to pray. He told God he was sorry. He told God he was ready to obey. And with that—*splat!* The fish spit Jonah out onto land. Jonah went to Nineveh, the city that had gone bad. And Nineveh believed Jonah's message. The whole city was saved, and God used Jonah to do it.

"When I was in the weeds," Jonah prayed, *"You, my God, came and saved me. When I was afraid, You heard my prayer."*

SEA CREATURES

Which sea creature below is not a fish? Circle it.

Color the whale. Find and color 2 seahorses, 5 spotted fish, and 5 striped fish. Draw more fish.

JONAH'S STORY

Find the 12 hidden words taken from the story of Jonah. They can be found up, down, across, backwards, and diagonally.

```
F U H R E Y A R P X G P
H O S R D F L E R S R U
E M R U S W A L L O W A
H J R G H T M L O Y H O
A G S A I L O R Y D A S
F R N E P V L R T T L Z
I N T R O N I D M U E S
S I H G R G B N D I A O
H N J M E S S A G E I R
Q E W F I E P G W S F R
P V T T W E V O O S I Y
E E M Q D W A N G R Y R
L H O K P M E E H B O T
```

WORD BOX

angry	Nineveh	sorry
fish	prayer	storm
forgiving	sailor	swallow
message	ship	whale

THE NEW TESTAMENT

Mary had just gotten some wonderful news. An angel named Gabriel had paid her a visit. "You are having a baby," Gabriel told her. "He will be the Son of God." Mary felt like the luckiest person on Earth.

There was only one problem. Mary was supposed to marry a man named Joseph. How was Joseph going to feel about Mary giving birth to God's Son?

Well, God took care of that. He sent an angel to Joseph, as well. The angel explained to Joseph that a gift was on it's way. "You shall call the baby Jesus," said the angel. Joseph listened carefully. When the time came, Joseph would take good care of Mary and of Jesus.

The time was very near. Mary rode on a donkey as Joseph led the way. All of the inns were full. They would stay the night in a stable instead.

THE ANGELS' VISITS

Which shadow belongs to the angel?

1   **2**   **3**

STORY QUIZ

Did you listen carefully to the story? Try to answer the following questions:

1. What was the name of the angel who visited Mary?

_____

2. What news did he bring to Mary?

_____

3. Who else had a visit from an angel? Why?

_____

DID YOU KNOW

Angel Gabriel also appeared to the prophet Daniel hundreds of years before and explained a vision to Daniel.

MARY AND JOSEPH

When they arrived in Bethlehem, Joseph and Mary found a stable to spend the night. Find where the stars fit into the picture and write that number there.

1 2 3 4 5

A King is Born
Matthew 1; Luke 2

On a clear and perfect night, Jesus Christ was born. This tiny baby was God's own Son. The Savior of the world had come to Earth.

Mary and Joseph wrapped Jesus in cloth. They laid Him in a manger on a soft bed of hay. The precious bundle slept away in peace. All around Him, the animals watched in wonder. Joseph and Mary looked down at Him full of love. And in Heaven above, the angels sang out with joy.

Unscramble the words of praise spoken by the angels of heaven to the shepherds who were watching their flocks. Use the code below.

A=1
B=2
C=3
D=4
E=5
F=6
G=7
H=8
I=9
J=10
K=11
L=12
M=13
N=14
O=15
P=16
Q=17
R=18
S=19
T=20
U=21
V=22
W=23
X=24
Y=25
Z=26

16 18 1 9 19 5   7 15 4   9 14
○ ○ ○ ○ ○ ○   ○ ○ ○   ○ ○

8 5 1 22 5 14 !   16 5 1 3 5
○ ○ ○ ○ ○ ○   ○ ○ ○ ○ ○

15 14   5 1 18 20 8   20 15
○ ○   ○ ○ ○ ○ ○   ○ ○

5 22 5 18 25 15 14 5   23 8 15
○ ○ ○ ○ ○ ○ ○ ○   ○ ○ ○

16 12 5 1 19 5 19   7 15 4 .
○ ○ ○ ○ ○ ○ ○   ○ ○ ○

Luke 2:14 CEV

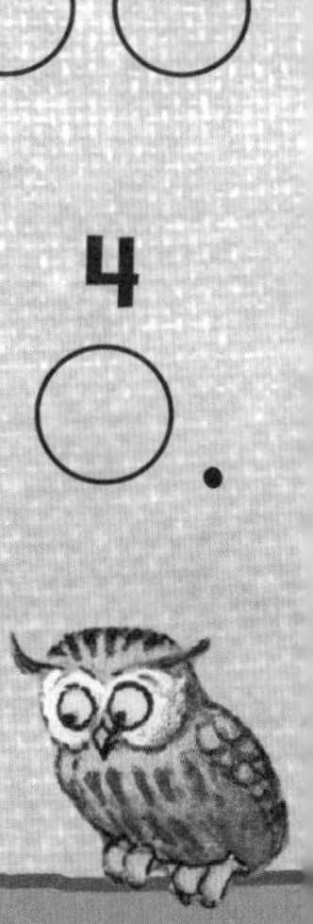

120

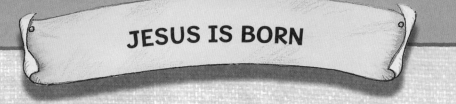

JESUS IS BORN

Find 10 differences in the two pictures.

"Wonderful is He!" sang the angels in Heaven the hour that Christ had come. "Almighty God, the Everlasting Father, the Prince of Peace!"

Three Wise Men

Matthew 2

In a land far away, three wise men saw a star. They knew just what the star meant. The King had been born, the Christ, who they had been waiting for.

They followed the star to where Jesus lay. When they saw Him, the wise men knelt down with joy. They gave Him precious gifts that they carried from the east . . . frankincense, gold, and sweet-smelling myrrh.

STAR OF BETHLEHEM

The wise men were guided by the bright star to find the King of the Jews. Which way did they take?

THE WISE MEN'S GIFTS

Each gift the wise men brought to Jesus was very precious. Each of these gifts was showing who Jesus is and what was His mission. Find the right description for the right picture.

• 1. MYRRH

• 2. GOLD

• 3. FRANKINCENSE

• A. was often a gift given to a king. It represents the fact that Jesus was royal and would rule the kingdom of God.

• B. is an aromatic resin that was used as incense in temples and churches. It was reserved for the worship of God. This gift represents the fact that Jesus was indeed divine.

• C. is an aromatic resin that was used for incense, perfume, and medicine. Its major use was for burials. It is said to represent that Jesus came into the world to die for our sins.

DID YOU KNOW

The wise men are also called the Magi. They were wise men from the east. The Bible does not say there were only three wise men. Tradition says that there were three because of the three gifts that were given to Jesus.

Fishers of Men
Matthew 4:18–26:75

Jesus grew up strong and good and wise. He was only twelve when He started teaching the teachers. Jesus knew more about the Kingdom of God than anyone else around. And He should have, of course, because Jesus was God's own Son.

When Jesus was all grown up, it was time to leave home. It was time to do God's work. Jesus went into the wilderness to pray for forty days. Afterwards, Jesus was strong, and He was ready.

Jesus needed helpers. He saw two men in a fishing boat. "Follow me," said Jesus, "and I will make you fishers of men." One by one, Jesus picked His friends who were brave and good, who wanted to serve God, and who were ready to share God's love. They would be called disciples. And wherever Jesus went, His disciples would follow.

Jesus said, "The Kingdom of God is like a net. It gathers all kinds of fish. The bad fish get tossed. The good fish get saved. Just like this, the good, the one's who believe in me, will join me in Heaven."

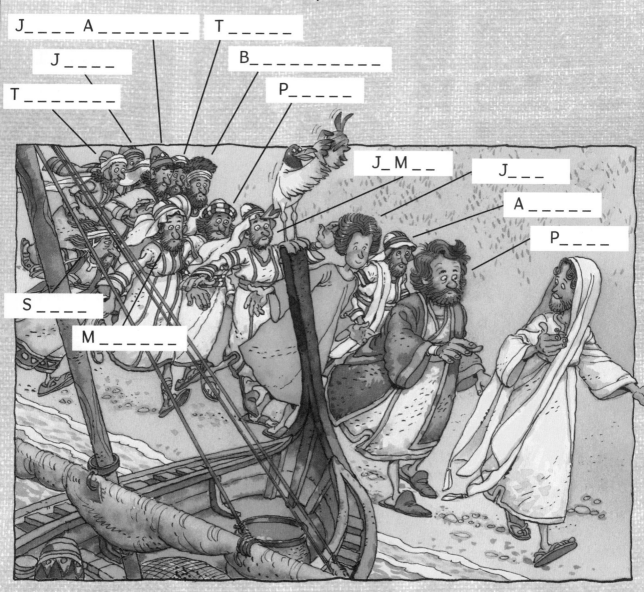

THE 12 DISCIPLES OF JESUS

Unscramble the names of the 12 disciples.

J_ _ _ _ A_ _ _ _ _ _ _ _

T_ _ _ _ _ _

J_ _ _ _

B_ _ _ _ _ _ _ _ _ _ _

T_ _ _ _ _ _ _

P_ _ _ _ _

J_ M _ _

J_ _ _

A_ _ _ _ _

P_ _ _ _

S_ _ _ _ _

M _ _ _ _ _ _ _

word box

Andrew	James Alphaeus	Matthew	Simon
Bartholomew	John	Peter	Thaddeus
James	Judas	Philip	Thomas

FOLLOWING JESUS

Find out what Jesus said to Simon and his brother Andrew by changing the bold letters to the next letter that comes in the alphabet.

IDRTR said to them, " **BNLD** with me! I will **SDZBG** you

....

how to **AQHMF** in people instead of **EHRG**." Mark 1:17 CEV

....

Color the areas with dots to find what symbol early Christians used as a secret Christian symbol.

DID YOU KNOW

The disciples had no extraordinary skills. They were ordinary people, but God chose them for a purpose. They left their homes, jobs, and friends to follow Jesus.

Love Your Enemy
Matthew 5

Everywhere that Jesus went, people came to see Him. Jesus told them stories. The stories that explained how to know good from bad. They showed the right ways to act and to always have love.

"Love your enemies," Jesus said. "And pray for those who hurt you. That's how you make your Father in Heaven glad. God sends the sunshine to good and bad alike. He sends rain to the wicked and the fair." Jesus said, "It is easy to love only those who love you." God won't reward you for that. But act like your Father in Heaven would and love both the nice and the mean.

Jesus said, "A farmer plants wheat, but his enemy sneaked in and planted weeds. When the wheat grew, the weeds grew with it, and the farmer put the wheat in barns but burned the weeds." This is what will happen to the people who know Jesus and the ones who don't when Jesus comes back.

LOVING EVERYONE

Find the 12 hidden words taken from the story of Love Your Enemy. They may be up, down, across, backwards, or diagonal.

```
G E F G R O W N D E
W G N C O P O B R N
L O V E E R A R A A
R O E D M A U N W M
L D O A E Y E H E O
S U N S H I N E R J
H R A H E A V E N E
C A S F A T H E R S
B E A U R I F U L U
W D E S T O R I E S
```

WORD BOX

enemy	heart	pray
Father	Heaven	reward
good	Jesus	stories
grow	love	sunshine

Can you find 10 grasshoppers in this picture?

Jesus told a story of a man who had two sons. The younger acted greedy and selfish. "I don't want to wait," he told his father. "I want the money you saved for me—right *now*." The father hated seeing his son upset. And so, the father agreed. *Clink, clink, clink,* the coins were counted out. Then boy went skipping away ready for some fun.

It wasn't long, not long at all. The money had not lasted like he thought it would when at first it was so heavy in his pocket. The boy was too ashamed to go home. So he took a job instead. He would shovel pig manure and eat with the pigs as well.

His stomach growled. The boy could not stand it a moment more; he was going to take his chances. Maybe his father would forgive him just enough to make him a servant.

When the father saw his son, he leaped out of the house. His beloved son was home safe and sound! He would not let him be a servant. This was his son, and he would be treated like one still. The father put him back in fine clothes and called for a feast.

"Just like this story," Jesus said, "your Father in Heaven forgives. God is glad when His precious child comes back home."

Here are 4 pictures of the son leaving his father. Two of them are exactly the same. Which two?

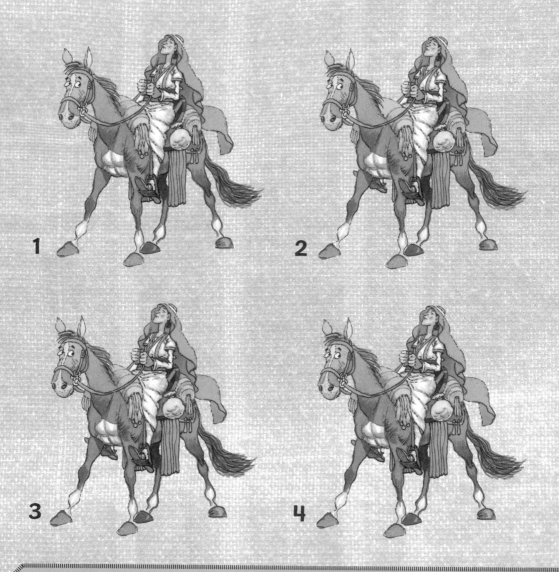

DID YOU KNOW

This story is also called the prodigal son. Prodigal means to spend a lot of money on things we don't need and to be very wasteful.

A FORGIVING FATHER

Unscramble the words spoken by the father to his older son, who didn't forgive his younger brother. Use the code below.

A=1	N=14
B=2	O=15
C=3	P=16
D=4	Q=17
E=5	R=18
F=6	S=19
G=7	T=20
H=8	U=21
I=9	V=22
J=10	W=23
K=11	X=24
L=12	Y=25
M=13	Z=26

2 21 20 23 5 19 8 15 21 12 4
B U T W E S H O U L D

2 5 7 12 1 4 1 14 4
B E G L A D A N D

3 5 12 5 2 18 1 20 5 !
C E L E B R A T E !

25 15 21 18 2 18 15 20 8 5 18
Y O U R B R O T H E R

23 1 19 4 5 1 4 ,
W A S D E A D ,

2 21 20 8 5 9 19
B U T H E I S

14 15 23 1 12 9 22 5 .
N O W A L I V E .

Luke 15:32 CEV

Water into Wine

"Thank goodness you're here," said Mary when Jesus arrived. There was a problem. "The wedding has run out of wine!" Mary cried. How embarrassing this would be for the bride and groom and with so many important guests.

Mary knew that her son was just the one to save the day. "Whatever Jesus tells you," said Mary to the servants, "do it."

Jesus asked for pitchers. He told them to fill each pitcher with water one by one. The servants took the pitchers to the table. Were they really supposed to fill up wine glasses with only water? With shaky hands, the servants started to pour. Yet instead of water, the pitchers poured out wine! Jesus had done his first miracle of many.

The master of the feast cleared his throat. He declared that this was the best wine yet!

"I am the true vine," said Jesus, "and my Father is the gardener. He cuts off the branches that don't have fruit. He keeps the rest healthy to make even more fruit."

139

WEDDING AT CANA

The wedding was taking place in Cana, a small village in Galilee. Weddings were very important celebrations among the Jewish people. Find out where the 5 pictures go, and write the number in the circle.

1

2

3

4

5

THE TRUE VINE

Jesus called himself the true vine. God is the gardener, and we are the . . .

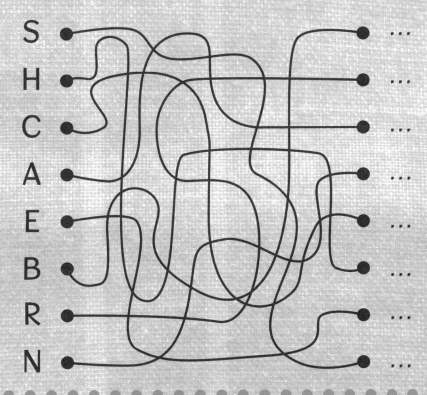

S
H
C
A
E
B
R
N

How many overlapping jars can you find here? _____

DID YOU KNOW
Turning water into wine at a wedding was Jesus' first miracle.

The Miracles of Jesus
Matthew 9; Mark 2; Luke 5

It had not taken long for the news to spread. This was no ordinary man. Jesus could make people walk who couldn't walk before. He could make the blind able to see. He could make the deaf able to hear. Jesus could heal anyone!

"Lord," called a sick man, "I believe You can heal me." Right away, the man was well. When Peter's mother got a fever, Jesus healed her with just a touch. Men with diseases went leaping away with joy. One woman touched only His robe, and she was made well.

One day, Jesus was in a house of doctors and lawyers. All of a sudden, the roof opened up. A man was lowered down with ropes—putting him right in front of Jesus. The house had been so full that the sick man's friends had to bring him in through the roof.

Jesus was amazed. What great friends the sick man had! Great friends with great faith. And that was all Jesus needed to see to heal the man.

HEALING THE SICK

Jesus showed love and compassion for others when he healed people. Color Jesus healing the sick man and the people witnessing the miracle.

DID YOU KNOW
The four Gospels record 37 miracles of Jesus, but Jesus did many other things as well that were not recorded.

Find out what Jesus said to the paralyzed man by changing the bold letters to the letters that come before them in the alphabet.

"**HFU VQ**! Pick up your **NBU** and go on **IPNF**." Mark 2:11 CEV

....

Jesus performed many miracles. Match the words to find some of Jesus' miracles.

TURNED WATER	THE SICK
DROVE OUT	TO LIFE
HEALED	THE STORM
RAISED	INTO WINE
CALMED	EVIL SPIRITS

The Great Storm

Mark 4:35-41

Things had gone from bad to worse. Giant waves now splashed aboard. It was time to wake up the boss. "Jesus," cried a disciple, "we are all going to *drown*!"

Jesus calmly got up. He went to the front of the boat where the storm whirled all around Him. Then He raised His hands toward the sea. "Peace!" said Jesus. "Be still." Right away, the storm obeyed. The wind died down. All was calm.

Jesus looked at His disciples. "Why were you afraid?" Jesus asked them. The disciples just stared back . . . Jesus had power even over the wind and sea!

Find 10 differences between the two pictures below.

CALMING THE STORM

Unscramble the words taken from the story of Jesus calming the storm, and use the clues to solve the crossword puzzle.

LITLS

PIDISCSEL

ACEEP

WEPOR

TROMS

NDOWR

VESAW

NWID

word box

STORM	PEACE
WAVES	STILL
DISCIPLES	WIND
DROWN	POWER

across

1. Jesus raised His hands and said, "________."
2. One of the disciples thought they were all going to ________.
3. There were giant ________ waves.
4. The ______ calmed down when Jesus commanded.
5. Jesus also told the sea to be ________.

down

1. Jesus has great ________.
2. The ________________ were afraid.
6. The ________ were splashing aboard.

The Endless Feast

Mark 6:39-44; John 6:8-15

The answer was not good. "We only have what this boy gave us," said a disciple, "two fish and five loaves of bread." How were they ever going to feed five thousand people? Worst of all, they were in the middle of a desert. Everyone wore a crinkled, worried face.

Everyone, that is, but Jesus. He held the food up and prayed. Then, Jesus began to break the bread and fish. Into large baskets, the pieces fell. One basket was soon full, then another . . . and another! Jesus filled basket after basket without ever running out. All of the people could now stuff themselves silly. And when no one could eat another bite, there were leftovers to save for later.

LOAVES AND FISH

Color the A's blue and the B's brown.
What is the picture? _____

FEEDING THE 5,000

Can you find and circle in the picture below:

1. three baskets 2. seven fish skeletons 3. two cats

154

Back from the Dead
John 11:1-44

Jesus felt His heart crack. Jesus had come too late. Lazarus was already dead. Jesus went to the cave where His good friend was buried, and He cried.

Yet—He was Jesus after all. "Take away the stone," Jesus ordered. Then, He looked up to Heaven. Jesus prayed to God, saying, "Father, thank You for hearing me."

What happened next was the most amazing miracle yet. "Lazarus!" called Jesus with a loud voice. "Come out of there." Lazarus stepped out of the cave just as alive as ever. His sisters ran to him crying with joy. And all who saw it believed.

"I tell you the truth," said Jesus. "It takes the tiniest bit of faith to do something amazing." Jesus taught His friends that they, too, could make a miracle. All they had to do was to believe. "If you had faith no bigger than a mustard seed," said Jesus, "then you could say to this mountain, 'Move from here, and go there.' And the mountain would obey you. If you just have faith, then nothing is impossible."

ON THE WAY TO LAZARUS

Mary and Martha sent for Jesus when their brother, Lazarus, got sick. Help Jesus find the way to Lazarus' home in Bethany.

DID YOU KNOW

Lazarus and his two sisters, Mary and Martha, were friends of Jesus.

A GREAT MIRACLE

Find the 12 hidden words taken from the story of Lazarus. They may be up, down, across, backwards, or diagonal.

```
G L M I R A C L E P
W A N C O P H B E E
L Z M F R I E N D V
R A E A M A A N S A
L R O I Z L V H T C
S U N T H I E E O G
D S A H E V N E N H
E A S F A E H G E S
A E B U R I E D L U
D D E S I S T E R S
```

WORD BOX

alive	dead	Lazarus
amazing	faith	miracle
buried	friend	sisters
cave	heaven	stone

Jesus Walks on Water
Mark 6:45-50; Matthew 14:22-33

The boat rocked back and forth. *If only Jesus were here*, thought the disciples. Jesus would stop the storm, and they'd be saved. But instead, the storm grew worse and worse.

Just then—what was that out on the sea? Through the darkness, the disciples saw the shape of a man. He was walking on the water . . . and coming *straight* for them. They were terrified—a *ghost*!

"Fear not," came the voice. "It's me, Jesus."

Peter wasn't so sure. "If it's really you," said Peter, "then let me walk out to You." Jesus agreed. So with shaky legs, Peter swung himself over the edge of the boat. He took one step, then another. Peter was walking on water! And in the middle of a scary storm too. Peter felt the wind tear at his hair. He looked across at the size of the waves. Then—*ker-splash*, Peter toppled into the water.

Jesus grabbed his hand. "Peter," said Jesus, "why did you not believe?"

"Ask, and it shall be given," said Jesus. "Look, and you will find it. Knock, and the door will open. The one who asks will get. The one who looks will find. To the one who knocks, the door will be opened."

"Listen," Jesus said. "If a child asks for bread, do the parents give a rock? No, all parents want to give their children something good. And that is the same way with your Father in Heaven."

JESUS AND PETER

Find out where the pieces of the puzzle go to reconstruct the picture.

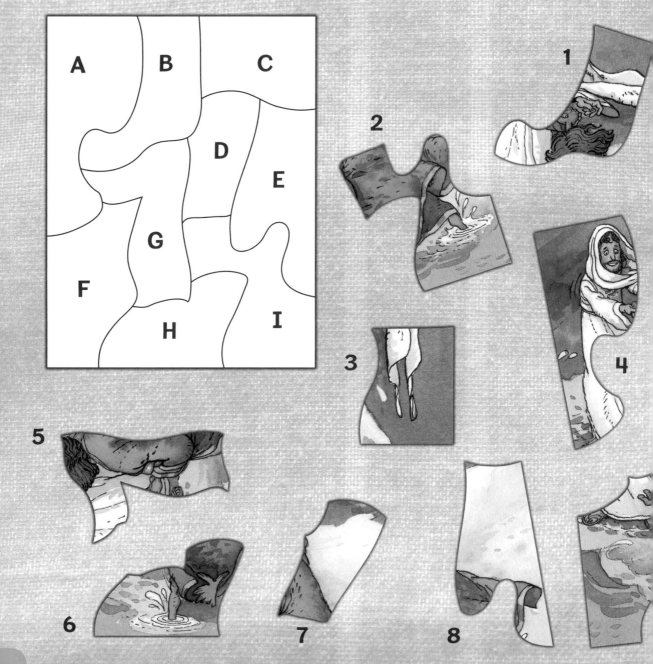

Use the code to unscramble the Bible verse below to find out what the disciples said to Jesus.

A=1
B=2
C=3
D=4
E=5
F=6
G=7
H=8
I=9
J=10
K=11
L=12
M=13
N=14
O=15
P=16
Q=17
R=18
S=19
T=20
U=21
V=22
W=23
X=24
Y=25
Z=26

20 8 5   13 5 14   9 14
◯ ◯ ◯   ◯ ◯ ◯   ◯ ◯

20 8 5   2 15 1 20
◯ ◯ ◯   ◯ ◯ ◯ ◯

23 15 18 19 8 9 16 5 4
◯ ◯ ◯ ◯ ◯ ◯ ◯ ◯ ◯

10 5 19 21 19   1 14 4   19 1 9 4
◯ ◯ ◯ ◯ ◯   ◯ ◯ ◯   ◯ ◯ ◯ ◯ ,

" 25 15 21   18 5 1 12 12 25   1 18 5
◯ ◯ ◯   ◯ ◯ ◯ ◯ ◯ ◯   ◯ ◯ ◯

20 8 5   19 15 14   15 6   7 15 4
◯ ◯ ◯   ◯ ◯ ◯   ◯ ◯   ◯ ◯ ◯ " .

Matthew 14:33 CEV

161

Let the Children Come

Mark 10:13-16

Everyone wanted to see Jesus. The mothers brought their little ones for Jesus to bless. The children crowded as close as they could get.

The disciples got annoyed. Jesus had important things to do! There were lessons to be taught. There were people to be healed. *Jesus did not have time to bother with kids,* thought His friends. So they tried to send all the children away.

Jesus saw what His friends were doing. And Jesus did not like it at all. "Do not send the children away," He told his friends. "Let them come to me because," said Jesus, "it is *children* who hold the keys to Heaven."

"Listen to me," said Jesus. "No one may enter God's Kingdom unless they come like a little child." They must not act high and mighty or think they know it all. Instead, the Kingdom of God is for those whose heart is pure. It is for those who can listen. It is for those who can believe.

JESUS AND THE CHILDREN

Jesus loves children. They are very special in His eyes. Color the scene of Jesus with the children below.

"COME TO ME"

Look at these pictures carefully. Which one is different?

Jesus also taught His disciples about what is important. Find out what He said to them by changing the bold letters to the next letter in the alphabet.

"If you want to be **FQDZS**, you must be the **RDQUZMS** of

....

all the **NSGDQR**." Mark 10:43 CEV

....

Hosanna to the King

Matthew 21:1-11

"Hosanna," called the people. Their King had come! They waved big branches of palm as Jesus passed by.

Jesus did not wear fancy robes. He did not ride a mighty stallion. Instead, Jesus wore plain robes and rode on a donkey that bumped along on the way to the city.

People had come out to see Him for miles around. This was the one who was going to save them from all troubles, they thought. They spread their clothes on the ground. They made His way fit for a king. "Hosanna," they cried. "Hosanna in the highest!"

"I am the way," said Jesus. "I am the truth and the life. No one can get to the Father except through me."

A TRIUMPHAL ENTRY

Can you find in this picture:
1. 29 palm branches
2. a woman playing tambourine
3. a man on a balcony

THE KING OF KINGS

Find these 4 words taken from the story: Hosanna, Branches, Donkey, Palm. Cross them out one letter at a time. You can go up, down, left or right, but the letters can be used only once.

➡️

H	O	D	K	E
A	S	O	N	Y
N	N	M	L	A
B	A	C	H	P
R	A	N	E	S

Which shadow belongs to Jesus on the donkey?

1   2   3

DID YOU KNOW
On Palm Sunday we celebrate Jesus' triumphal entry into Jerusalem. Palm Sunday is the Sunday before Easter.

Jesus broke the bread and handed it to his apostles. Then he said, "This is my body, which is given for you. Eat this as a way of remembering me!"

The Last Supper

Luke 22:14-46

Jesus had a heavy heart. It was the last time He would eat with His friends.

He passed around His cup and broke the bread. He told His friends to remember Him whenever they ate from now on. "Whoever shall be the greatest," said Jesus, "may that person act like the smallest. And whoever shall be the chief, act like a servant."

After supper, Jesus went to pray in the garden. "Dear Father," said Jesus, "may Your plan be done."

JESUS' LAST MEAL

Draw a line to connect the zoomed-in, black-and-white pictures to where they belong in the picture. Then color them.

DID YOU KNOW

At the Last Supper, Jesus showed humility by doing the task that no one wanted to do. He washed the disciples' feet. Washing someone's feet was considered a dirty job. Only servants washed people's feet.

IN THE GARDEN

Which path did Jesus take from the upper room in Jerusalem, where He had his last supper, to the Garden of Gethsemane, where He went to pray.

Soldiers at the Garden Gate

John 18:1-14; Matthew 26:47-68

Jesus and His friends were just leaving the garden when they saw a terrible sight. A group of soldiers—coming *straight* towards them.

Peter wanted to fight the soldiers. He drew his sword.

"Put that away," said Jesus. "This is God's plan." Jesus acted brave. He went with the soldiers without fighting at all.

Jesus was taken before a rowdy crowd. "Kill Him!" they yelled. It was a terrible thing to hear for someone who loved people so much.

PETER FOUGHT BACK

Trying to protect Jesus, Peter drew a sword and attacked a man named Malchus, the servant of the high priest, chopping off his ear. Jesus stopped Peter and healed the man's ear. Color the scene.

DID YOU KNOW
The trial of Jesus took place in six stages: three before the Jewish elders and three before the Gentile authorities.

THE TRIAL OF JESUS

Following His arrest, Jesus was put on trial and sentenced to death.
Find 10 differences between the two pictures.

Jesus had been locked up. Now Peter stood alone warming his hands at a fire.

"Hey, you," a voice called. Peter looked up. Nearby, a group of soldiers stood alert, their swords glittering. Were the soldiers going to take Peter away like they had taken Jesus?

The woman spoke again. "Did I not see you with Jesus?" she asked.

"Who, me?" said Peter ducking away.

But Peter did not get far. "That one, there!" said another. "That man is a friend of Jesus."

Peter could feel eyes burn into him from every side. The fear was starting to boil. Peter shook his head. "You have the wrong guy," he replied. A third time someone asked him if he was a follower of Jesus, and for the third time, Peter said no. Then Peter hurried off.

Just then . . . cock-a-doodle-do! The cry of a rooster shook Peter to his senses. Suddenly, Peter realized—he had lied. Peter had pretended not to be a friend of Jesus when it mattered the most. Peter's heart filled with sadness, more sorry than words.

Jesus had told his friends what would happen. "The time has come," He had said, "that each will go off alone. Yet I will not be alone since the Father is with Me."

179

PETER' DENIAL

Find the 12 hidden words taken from the story of Peter. They may be up, down, across, backwards, or diagonal.

```
D U S R E I D L O S
N A R O S W O R D S
E N O F A T H E R S
I W O M A N P H O S
R E S S U S E J U E
F L T D E A T R N N
C S E C O L E F T D
F I R E P O R E A A
R A M F R N E A I S
L R E P Z E V R N E
```

WORD BOX

alone	friend	sadness
Father	Jesus	soldiers
fear	Peter	swords
fire	rooster	woman

THE ROOSTER CROWED

Which silhouette matches the picture of Peter?

1

2

3

4

5

MEMORY GAME

Study the picture of Peter denying Jesus on page 178 and 179. Now try to answer these questions without looking back.

1. How many mice are warming up by the fire? _____

2. How many spear(s) are there in the picture? _____

3. What do you see at the top right of the picture? _____

4. Who can you see in the far back in the picture? _____

The Cross on the Hill

Luke 23:32-46

Jesus had known He would die from the very beginning. It was the only way to save the world from sin. It was the only way He could pay our way to Heaven.

They hung Jesus on a cross high on a hill. Jesus looked up to Heaven. He prayed that God would forgive those who had hurt Him. Then Jesus closed His eyes, and it was done.

JESUS ON THE CROSS

Jesus willingly died on the cross because He loved us so much. Seek and find these things in the picture below:

Find out a very important Bible verse by changing the bold letters to the letter that comes before it in the alphabet.

HPE loved the **QFPQMF** of this world **TP NVDI** that

....

he gave his only **TPO**, so that **FWFSZPOF** who has

....

GBJUI in him will have **FUFSOBM** life and never

....

really **EJF**. (John 3:16 CEV)

....

How many overlapping crosses can you count here?

185

A Cave for a King

John 19:31-34; Matthew 27:57-61

Jesus had died. His friends washed and perfumed Him. They wanted to give Jesus the best burial that they could. But a nice burial was going to cost money . . . a lot of money.

A rich man named Joseph came to the rescue. He wrapped Jesus up in fine, white cloth. He gave his brand-new cave for the burial. Inside the cave, Jesus was laid to rest. Each said their goodbyes. Then, a stone was rolled over the cave. His friends would miss Jesus forever and always. Yet His words were tucked in their hearts to warm them with love.

Of course, not everyone was sorry Jesus had died. After a day had passed, the rulers began to worry. Had Jesus not said that He would rise again?

The rulers were not taking chances. They made sure the cave was sealed up good and tight. Then they put soldiers outside to keep watch. No one was getting in or out.

So they thought. Yet God always has the final say. And nothing can be hidden that God wants brought to light.

"For a little while, you will not see me," Jesus had told His friends. "Yet a little while more, and you will see me again.

"When I'm gone, you will cry with sadness. Yet your sorrow will turn to joy. You will see me again with a gladness that no one can take away."

JESUS' FRIENDS

One of the women present at Jesus' burial was . . .

Y ●   ● . . .

M ●   ● . . .

A ●   ● . . .

R ●   ● . . .

A ●   ● . . .

D ●   ● . . .

E ●   ● . . .

L ●   ● . . .

N ●   ● . . .

M ●   ● . . .

A ●   ● . . .

E ●   ● . . .

G ●   ● . . .

THE BURIAL OF JESUS

Color the picture below of Jesus and His friends taking care of Him.

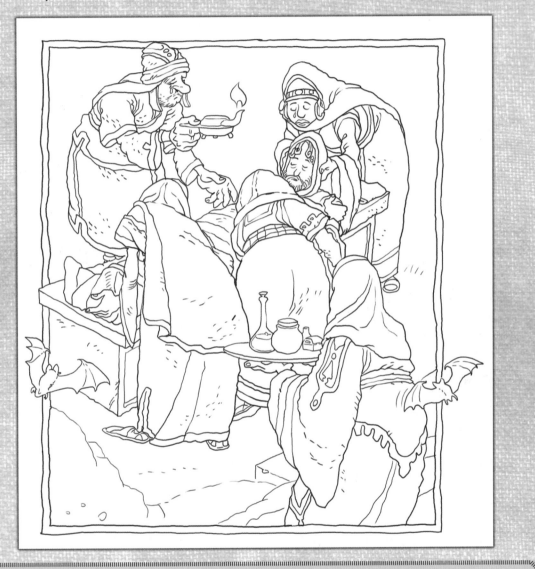

DID YOU KNOW

The two men who buried Jesus' body were Joseph of Arimathea and Nicodemus. They wrapped Jesus' body in linen with spices according to the Jewish customs and buried it in the tomb that belonged to Joseph.

Jesus is Alive
Matthew 28:1-10

Mary and her friends got up early. It was the third day since Jesus had died. Time to go and visit the cave. The women headed down the road just as the sun began to rise.

All of a sudden, the ground shook. The earth roared. The women could barely keep their balance—it was an *earthquake!* They rushed to the cave.

There sat a beautiful, shining someone on top of a rock. It was an angel who had rolled the stone away that had closed the cave.

"Don't be afraid," said the angel. "I know you came to see Jesus. But Jesus is no longer here . . . He is risen, alive."

"All hail," said a voice. The three women had been running to tell their friends about the angel. But now someone blocked the road. It was Jesus. "Go tell the others," He said to Mary and her friends. "Tell them I am alive. And that they will soon see me, as well."

AT THE CAVE

Unscramble the words taken from the story and use the clues to solve the crossword puzzle.

ECAV

NTOSE

VALEI

GALEN

OMWEN

SEUJS

DIRFENS

KERHTAUEQA

word box

ALIVE   FRIENDS
ANGEL   JESUS
CAVE   STONE
EARTHQUAKE   WOMEN

across

1. The messenger sitting on the top of the rock.
2. The _____ made the ground shake.
3. Jesus' _____ went to visit the cave.
4. Mary and her friends were all _____.

down

5. The angel rolled the _____ away.
6. _____ is risen.
7. Jesus was buried in a _____.
8. Jesus is not dead, He is _____!

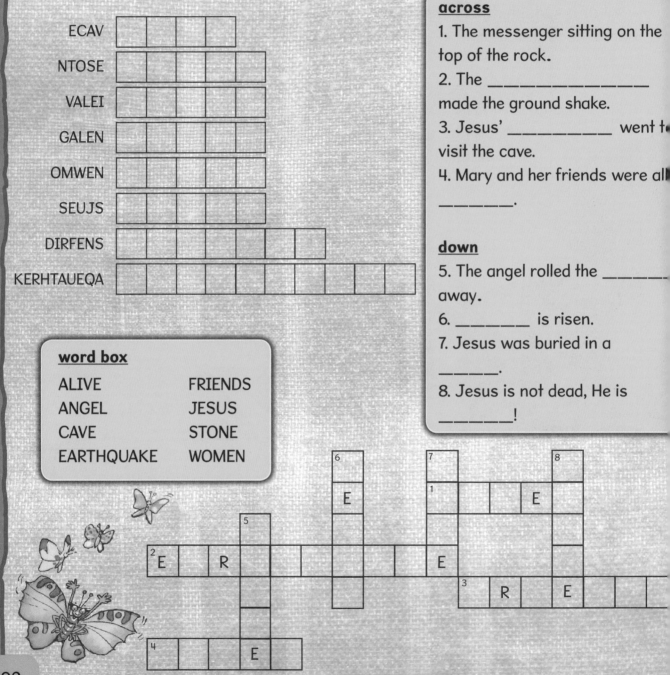

MARY MAGDALENE

Look carefully at the pictures of Mary Magdalene. Which two are exactly the same?

1   2   3

4   5   6

DID YOU KNOW

Mary Magdalene traveled with Jesus as one of his followers. She supported Jesus in his final moments and stayed with him at the cross. She was at his burial, and she was the first person to see Jesus after his Resurrection.

The Visitor

John 20:19-29

The disciples had just sat down to eat when they heard someone speak. "Peace be with you," said the voice. The disciples looked up from their plates. There, standing in front of them, was Jesus!

Thomas had heard that Jesus had risen and that Mary and the others had seen Him alive from the dead. And now Thomas was seeing Jesus for himself.

His friends could see the marks where He was nailed to the cross. Jesus said to Thomas, "Touch me, and believe." Thomas reached out a shaky finger. So—it *was* true! They all laughed and cried, both at the same time.

Jesus had come with a message. "I am giving you a special job," He said to His friends. "I want you to go tell the world just how much God loves them."

"Now you believe," said Jesus to Thomas, "because you have seen for yourself. But those who believe without needing to see, they are the ones truly blessed."

DOUBTING THOMAS

Find out where the 5 pictures go and write down the correct number in the space.

1

2

3

4

5

DID YOU KNOW

The disciple Thomas was also known as Didymus (Greek meaning "twin"). But the Bible doesn't tell us who was his twin. After the Resurrection of Jesus, he became a great missionary in India.

Unscramble the words to know what Jesus said to Thomas. Use the code below.

A=1
B=2
C=3
D=4
E=5
F=6
G=7
H=8
I=9
J=10
K=11
L=12
M=13
N=14
O=15
P=16
Q=17
R=18
S=19
T=20
U=21
V=22
W=23
X=24
Y=25
Z=26

16 21 20 25 15 21 18 8 1 14 4

"(P)(U)(T) (Y)(O)(U)(R) (H)(A)(N)(D)

9 14 20 15 13 25 19 9 4 5

(I)(N)(T)(O) (M)(Y) (S)(I)(D)(E).

19 20 15 16 4 15 21 2 20 9 14 7

(S)(T)(O)(P) (D)(O)(U)(B)(T)(I)(N)(G)

1 14 4 8 1 22 5

(A)(N)(D) (H)(A)(V)(E)

6 1 9 20 8

(F)(A)(I)(T)(H)!"

John 20:27 CEV

Cloud of Heaven

Acts 1:3-11

It was time for Jesus to go be with God. He gathered His friends on a mountain for a final farewell.

"Once I am gone, wait on God," said Jesus. God was going to pour out His Holy Spirit on them. Then they would be strong for the work to come. His friends still had questions. *Was God going to help their nation?* they wondered. Jesus answered, "It is not for you to know God's time or season." They would get what they needed though; Jesus promised. They were to spread all He had told them to the ends of the Earth.

Jesus started to rise up before their eyes. A beautiful cloud picked Him up. Higher and Higher, Jesus rose. Then, he was gone. Two men in white appeared among them and said that Jesus would come back again just like he left.

"In my Father's house are many rooms," Jesus said. "I am going there to make a place for you. One day, I will come again to take you there myself. So where I live, you will live there too."

FAREWELL

Find 10 differences between these two pictures.

JESUS ROSE UP

Find the 12 hidden words taken from the story of Jesus rising up. They may be up, down, across, backwards, or diagonal.

```
F S D N E I R F O G
D A R O O M S A N H
D N R F A E H T M O
U G B E R I E H O U
O E O H W S T E U S
L L M D E E C R N E
C S T C O A L B T C
L O I A J Y V L A A
R A M F O N E E I D
L R E E Z L V H N E
```

WORD BOX

angels	Father	house
cloud	friends	mountain
come	God	time
farewell	heaven	rooms

The Wicked Leader

Acts 8:1-4; 9:1-18

The leader named Saul had enough. Just who did these friends of Jesus think they were anyway? Telling people *who* and *what* to obey. Well, Saul had a way to make them quiet. He was going to go and arrest each and every last one.

Suddenly, a blast of blinding light made Saul fall from his horse, unable to see. "Saul, Saul . . . " came a voice. "Why do you fight against me?"

"Who are you?" Saul cried. Even with his eyes open, Saul could only see blackness. The mighty leader now felt afraid.

"I am Jesus," said the voice. Jesus told Saul to go into the city and wait. Saul obeyed. His servants led their blind master to where Jesus had said. For three days and nights, Saul did not eat. He did not drink. And he did not see anything but blackness all around him.

At last, the door creaked open. God had sent Ananias to help Saul. Ananias prayed, and Saul could see again. Saul stood up full of joy! He wanted to be baptized right away because Saul had work to do. He was going to tell the whole wide world about Jesus and all the good things of God for those who believed.

Saul was a new man. So he got a new name too - Paul, a friend of Jesus.

ON THE ROAD TO DAMASCUS

Help Paul find the way to Damascus where he was blinded by the light along the way.

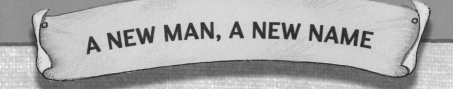

A NEW MAN, A NEW NAME

How many times can you find the word PAUL in this grid? It can be up, down, across, backwards, and diagonally.

P	A	U	L	■
A	A	■	L	P
U	L	U	A	P
L	A	U	L	■
P	L	U	A	P

The word PAUL can be found _____ times.

DID YOU KNOW

Saul/Paul was born into a Jewish family. His father was a Roman citizen, so he was too. He had 2 names: the Hebrew name Saul and the Latin name Paul. At that time, it was very common to have 2 names. When he began his missionary work to the Gentiles, he started to use his Roman name, Paul.

Earthquake at the Jail

Acts 9:20-31; 16:16-40

Paul proved how much he loved God. Paul would do whatever it took to spread the good news. *Even* if it meant going to jail. And that is exactly what lay in store for those who tried to change the rules.

Paul and Silas were chained, it was true. Yet their hearts burst with freedom for knowing God's love. The other prisoners heard a song break out. It was Paul and Silas praising God.

Crack! The walls started shaking. *Click*—the cell doors flew open as if by themselves. With a great loud *clank,* their chains all dropped to the ground.

The prison guard was terrified. What must he do—he begged to know—to be *saved*? Paul and Silas were happy to help. "Just believe in Jesus," they told him. The guard invited them to his house to have a bath and a meal. Then Paul and Silas baptized him and all his family.

IN PRISON

Find out the 2 mystery words by finding the missing letter of each vertical word.

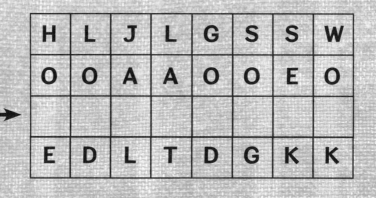

H	L	J	L	G	S	S	W
O	O	A	A	O	O	E	O
E	D	L	T	D	G	K	K

H	E	B	S	S	S	G	C	S	C
A	G	E	O	A	U	A	B	I	L
R	L	A	N	K	I	R	L	E	L
T	E	K	E	E	D	D	E	R	O

OUT OF JAIL

Find the right path from the prison to the guard's house.

The Shipwreck

Acts 26-28

Paul was in chains . . . again. He had not obeyed orders. He had not stopped teaching about Jesus. So now Paul was put on a ship to sail for a distant land.

Things at sea were looking dark. A mighty storm howled as huge waves splashed the deck. The sailors were certain they were all going to die . . . when their prisoner stood up.

Paul had something to say. "Don't be afraid," said Paul. He had dreamed of an angel who was keeping watch. "God is going to save each and every one of us," Paul told the crew.

There were few other choices but to take Paul's advice. He said there was no need to save food. The sailors watched Paul take a huge bite of bread. Then they all joined in. At least they could enjoy a final feast before the storm sank their ship.

Just then—what was that on the horizon? An island! Paul and the crew swam for shore. The friendly natives built a fire while Paul told about Jesus. When they were ready to set sail, Paul and the sailors said goodbye to their new friends and kept sailing to Rome.

Paul sent letters to the friends he had made. "Nothing can keep us," he wrote, "from the good love of God."

ON THE BOAT

Paul traveled on a ship. Use the grid to help you draw one, square by square. Then, color in it!

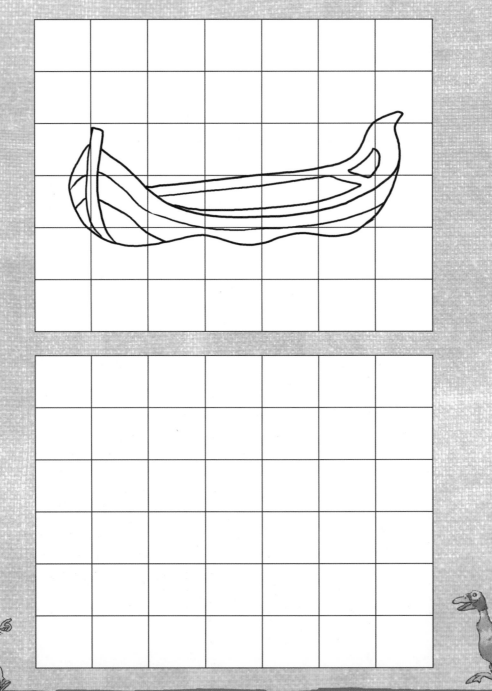

SAFE ON THE ISLAND

Complete the patterns and find out the name of the island.

P - R - Y - M - P - R - Y - M - P - R - Y - (__)

Z - I - I - A - Z - I - I - A - Z - I - I - (__)

U - L - U - K - U - L - U - K - U - (__)

O - T - T - O - T - T - O - T - T - O - (__)

H - E - G - A - H - E - G - A - H - E - G - (__)

The name is: __ __ __ __ __.

DID YOU KNOW

Paul went on many missionary journeys after he became a believer, including three long missionary journeys throughout the Roman Empire.

The World to Come

Micah 4:3; Revelation 7, 21

John dreamed that one day, Jesus would come again. On that day, all wars would end. Weapons would be turned into garden tools. Each person would sit under their own tree in peace.

On that day, all things would be made new. Those who believed would see Jesus at last. And people from every nation would sing out in joy.

215

JOHN'S DREAM

Find 16 crabs hidden in the picture below.

ABOUT REVELATION

Revelation was written by John, the apostle who had been one of Jesus' disciples. While he was held on a prison island called Patmos, John received a vision from Jesus. He wrote what he saw in this book that we call Revelation, the last book of the Bible.

JESUS WILL COME BACK

Unscramble an important verse from the book of Revelation using the code below.

✳ = A	❖ = I	⊖ = U
⌘ = E	⊠ = O	

Th⌘ L⊠rd G⊠d s✳ys, "❖ ✳m ✳lph✳ ✳nd ⊠m⌘g✳, th⌘ ⊠n⌘ wh⊠

Th_ L_rd G_d s_ys, "_ _m _lph_ _nd _m_g_, th_ _n_ wh_

❖s ✳nd w✳s ✳nd ❖s c⊠m❖ng. ❖ ✳m G⊠d ✳ll-P⊠w⌘rf⊖l!"

_s _nd w_s _nd _s c_m_ng. _ _m G_d _ll-P_w_rf_l!"

Revelation 1:8, CEV

How many words can you make with the letters from REVELATION?

_____

_____

_____

_____

_____

The Promise
Revelation 21

In Heaven God will wipe away all our tears. There will be no more sadness. There will be no pain. Those who trusted in Jesus and lived for Him on Earth... But those who did not believe but did wrong on Earth shall be sent away. Heaven will shine bright with the glory of God. The streets will be gold. The gates will be pearls.

   In Heaven there will be no sun or moon. Jesus alone will be our light. People from everywhere will sing of God's goodness. And believers will live in joy forever and ever.

"I am the beginning," says God, *"and I am the end. I was there at the first, and I will be there at the last."*

GOD'S GOODNESS

Can you find 10 differences between the two pictures?

LIVING IN JOY

Make your very own illustration of Heaven. You can use markers, glitter, collage . . .

REMEMBER
The only way to Heaven is through Jesus. Jesus forgives our sins when we ask Him for forgiveness and invite Him into our hearts.

GAME SOLUTIONS

THE OLD TESTAMENT

(pages 10-11) In the Beginning
The answers are: Mars, Neptune, Uranus, Jupiter, Venus, Earth, Mercury, Saturn.

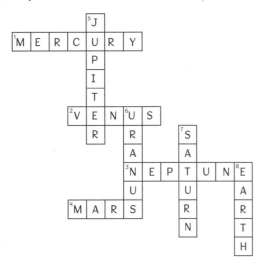

The answers are (from top to bottom): Venus, Mercury, Earth, Mars, Jupiter, Neptune, Saturn, Uranus.

(pages 14-15) God Brings Life
Penguin number 6 is the one that is different.

GOD MAKES THE ANIMALS.
The answers are: Earth, fish, birds, animals.

The names of the animals and birds are:
1. Dolphin, Zebra, Horse, Rabbit
2. Donkey, Chicken, Beaver, Camel
3. Snake, Panda, Ostrich, Penguin
4. Tiger, Peacock, Seagull, Turtle

(pages 18-19) Adam & Eve

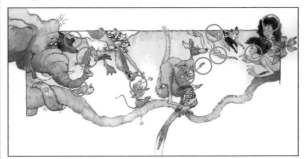

(pages 22-23) Two Brothers
The word is: sacrifice.

The word "lamb" can be found 8 times.

(pages 26-27) God Calls on Noah

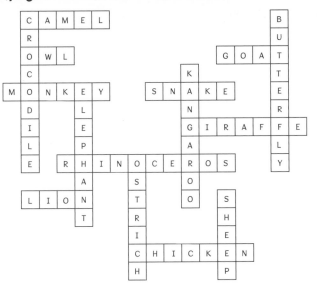

(pages 30-31) The Great Flood

The compound words are: sailboat and rawboat.

There are 10 boats in the drawing.

STORY QUIZ: 1. 40 days; 2. A dove.

(pages 34-35) Promise in a Rainbow

(pages 38-39) The Tower of Babel

The word is loving.

The tower 2 is different.

(pages 42-43) Abraham & Sarah

The synonyms are: land/region; bivouac/camp; promise/commitment; trust/faith; desert/wasteland.

(pages 46-47) Abraham's Great Big Family
SARAH was the wife of Abraham.
ISAAC was the only son Abraham and Sarah had.
JACOB was the son of Isaac and Rebekah.
ABRAHAM is the "father of many nations".

(pages 50-51) A Coat of Many Colors
A COLORFUL COAT
The answer is: "When Joseph came to his brothers, they pulled off his fancy coat."

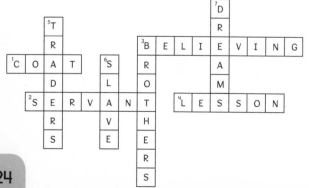

(pages 54-55) The Faith of Joseph

The name of Joseph's younger brother is: Benjamin.

(pages 58-59) The Baby in a Basket

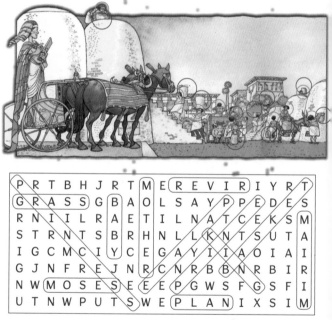

Baby Moses 3 is different.

(pages 62-163) The Burning Bush
RUNNING AWAY
The answer is: Moses ran to hide in a region called MIDIAN. There he married a woman called Zipporah and became a SHEPHERD, and

took care of many ANIMALS.

```
M I A M A
Z R I R A
I P P O N
A R O H R
H J E T O
```

(pages 66-67) Journey Through the Sea

The answers are: frogs, people, slaves, smoke, staff, army, problem, waves.

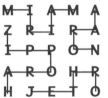

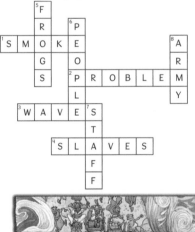

(pages 70-71) The Promised Land
BECOMING A LEADER

The answer is: "I've commanded you to be strong and brave."

(pages 74-75) Gideon Wants Proof

The answers are: soldier 2, camel 4 and soldier on the camel 1.

(pages 78-79) Samson the Strong

Dot-to-dot: a lion.

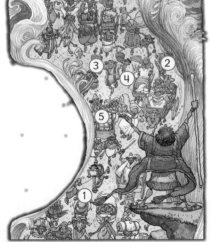

SAMSON'S STRENGTHS

The words are:
1. strong, courageous, supernatural, powerful
2. robust, capable, vigorous, solid

(pages 82-83) Ruth's Reward

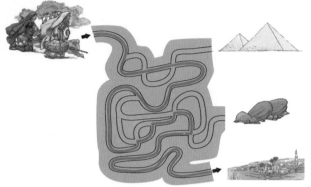

LOYALTY
The answer is: "Your people will be my people, your God will be my God."

(pages 86-87) The Shepherd Boy
The shape is a bear.
Shadow 3 matches the shape.

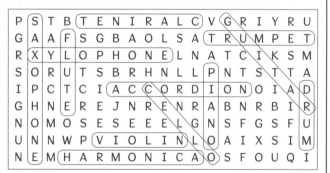

(pages 90-91) David & Goliath

(pages 94-95) The Wisest King

Shadow 2 belongs to the man holding the baby.

Facts about God's temple. The answer is: In the FOURTH year of his reign, Solomon began the CONSTRUCTION of the Temple. SEVEN years later it was completed, and the ARK of the COVENANT was moved to the Temple.

(pages 98-99) Elijah the Prophet
The answers are: bread, famine, ravens, brook, message, woman, prophet, flour.

(pages 102-103) Esther, Brave & Fair
There are 17 overlapping crowns.

Esther's uncle's name is: Mordecai.

(pages 106-107) The Lions' Den

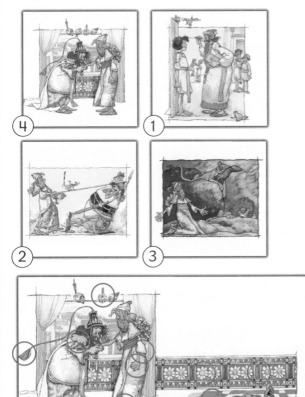

(pages 110-111) Jonah & the Whale
The sea creature that is not a fish is:

```
F U H R E Y A R P X G P
H O S R D F L E R S R U
E M R U S W A L L O W A
H J R G H T M L O Y H O
A G S A I L O R Y D A S
F R N E P V L R T T L Z
I N T R O N I D M U E S
S I H G R G B N D I A O
H N J M E S S A G E I R
Q E W F I E P G W S F R
P V T T W E V O O S I Y
E E M Q D W A N G R Y R
L H O K P M E E H B O T
```

THE NEW TESTAMENT
(pages 116-117) Mary & Joseph
STORY QUIZ
1. Angel Gabriel
2. She was going to give birth to God's only Son.
3. Joseph also had a visit from an angel, who explained to Joseph what was going to happen.

(pages 120-121) A King is Born
THE NATIVITY STORY
The answer is: "Praise God in heaven! Peace on earth to everyone who pleases God."

(pages 124-125) Three Wise Men

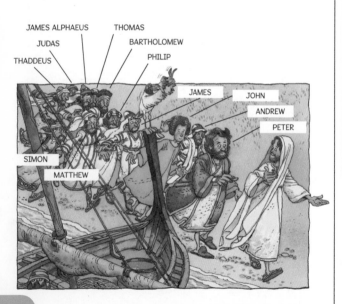

THE WISE MEN'S GIFTS
The answers are: 1. C.; 2. A.; 3. B.

(pages 128-129) Fishers of Men

JAMES ALPHAEUS
JUDAS
THADDEUS
THOMAS
BARTHOLOMEW
PHILIP
JAMES
JOHN
ANDREW
PETER
SIMON
MATTHEW

FOLLOWING JESUS
The answer is: "JESUS said to them, "COME with me! I will TEACH you how to BRING in people instead of FISH".

Color the dots: a fish.

(pages 132-133) Love Your Enemy

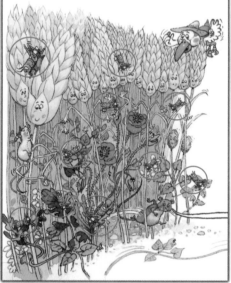

(pages 136-137) The Loving Father
Pictures 3 and 4 are exactly the same.

A FORGIVING FATHER
The answer is: "But we should be glad and celebrate! Your brother was dead, but he is

now alive."

(pages 140-141) Water into Wine

THE TRUE VINE
The answer is: branches.

There are 9 overlapping jars.

(pages 144-145) The Miracles of Jesus
JESUS' MIRACLES
The answer is: "GET UP! Pick up your MAT and go on HOME".

The miracles are: Jesus turned water into wine, drove out evil spirits, healed the sick, raised to life, calmed the storm.

(pages 148-149) The Great Storm

CALMING THE STORM
The answers are: still, disciples, peace, power, storm, drown, waves, wind.

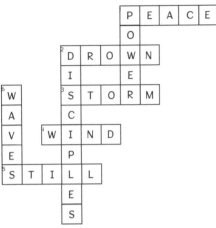

(pages 152-153) The Endless Feast
LOAVES AND FISH
You will find 2 fish and 5 breads.

(pages 156-157) Back from the Dead

(pages 160-161) **Jesus Walks on Water**

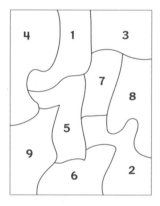

JESUS' MIRACULOUS POWER
The answer is: "The men in the boat worshipped Jesus and said, 'You really are the Son of God.'"

(pages 164-165) **Let the Children Come**
Picture 2 is different.

Jesus' words are: "If you want to be GREAT, you must be the SERVANT of all the OTHERS."

(pages 168-169) **Hosanna to the King**

Shadow 2 belongs to Jesus on the donkey.

(pages 172-173) **The Last Supper**

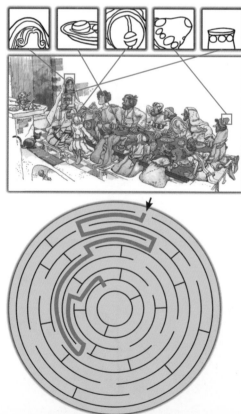

(pages 176-177) Soldiers at the Garden Gate

(pages 180-181) Peter Denies

Silhouette 5 matches Peter.

MEMORY GAME
1. Two; 2. One; 3. A man pointing at Peter; 4. Jesus.

(pages 116-117) The Cross on the Hill

JESUS DIED FOR OUR SINS
The answer is: "God loved the PEOPLE of this world SO MUCH that he gave his only SON, so that EVERYONE who has FAITH in him will have ETERNAL life and never really DIE."

There are 11 overlapping crosses.

(pages 188-189) A Cave for a King
One of the women present at Jesus' burial was Mary Magdalene.

(pages 192-193) Jesus is Alive
The answers are: cave, stone, alive, angel, women, Jesus, friends, earthquake.

The pictures of Mary Magdalene 2 and 4 are exactly the same.

(pages 196-197) The Visitor

231

FAITH
The answer is: "Put your hand into my side. Stop doubting and have faith!"

(pages 200-201) Cloud of Heaven

(pages 204-205) The Wicked Leader

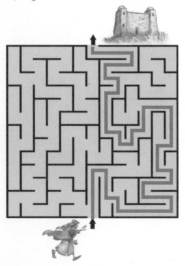

The word "Paul" can be found 7 times.

(pages 208-209) Earthquake at the Jail
The 2 mystery words are: prisoner, earthquake.

OUT OF JAIL
The right path is 1.

(pages 212-213) The Shipwreck
The name of the island is Malta.

(pages 216-217) The World to Come

JESUS WILL COME BACK
The answer is: "The Lord God says, "I am alpha and omega, the one who is and was and is coming. I am God all-powerful!"

Some of the words you can make with the letters from "REVELATION": elevation, interval, elevator, relative, relevant, eternal, trainee, reveal, tailor, alive, real, tan, on, in, late, lion, vale, tail, tale, rat, lean, veal, rate, train, tree.

(pages 220-221) The Promise

Once-a-Month
COOKING

A proven system for spending less time

in the kitchen and enjoying delicious,

homemade meals everyday

MIMI WILSON AND MARY BETH LAGERBORG

BROADMAN
&HOLMAN
PUBLISHERS

Nashville, Tennessee

© 1986, 1992, 1999 by Mimi Wilson and Mary Beth Lagerborg
Printed in the United States of America

0-8054-1835-0

Published by Broadman & Holman Publishers, Nashville, Tennessee
Editorial Team: Vicki Crumpton, Janis Whipple, Kim Overcash
Page Design: Paul T. Gant Art & Design
Typesetting: PerfecType, Nashville, Tennessee

Published in 1986 by St. Martin's Press. Second edition in 1992 published by
Focus on the Family Publishing. This book was originally published in 1982
under the title *Freeze and Save* and in 1984 as *Dinner's Ready*.

Dewey Decimal Classification: 641.5
Subject Heading: MAKE-AHEAD COOKERY / COOKING / FAMILY
Library of Congress Card Catalog Number: 98-40917

Unless otherwise stated all Scripture citation is from the NIV, the Holy Bible, New
International Version, copyright © 1973, 1978, 1984 by International Bible Society; other
versions include The Living Bible (TLB), copyright © 1971 by Tyndale House Publishers.

Library of Congress Cataloging-in-Publication Data

Wilson, Marilyn S., 1946–
    Once-a-month cooking / Marilyn S. Wilson, Mary E. Lagerborg.
        p. cm.
    Originally published: 1992.
    Includes index.
    ISBN 0-8054-1835-0 (pbk.)
    1. Make-ahead cookery. I. Lagerborg, Mary Beth. II. Title.
TX652.W5647   1999
641.5'55—dc21

                                                                98-40917
                                                                CIP

9 10 11 12   05 04

Dedication

Our most expert—and honest—recipe testers

Calvin Wilson	Alex Lagerborg
Kurt and Lori Wilson	Tim Lagerborg
Tom and Kyndra Trinidad	Dan Lagerborg
Kevin Wilson	Andrew Lagerborg

DEDICATION

Table of Contents

TABLE OF CONTENTS

Acknowledgments

Our warmest thanks to family and friends who have contributed recipes, table talk questions, and their perspective to this edition of *Once-a-Month Cooking:*

Kurt Wilson
Lori Wilson
Renee Loring
Sue Herd
Cynthia Bahlman
Capt. Lois True
Ginger Brown
Linnea Rein
Sandi Hanson
Cala Doolittle
Marge Rodemer
Alice Tate

INTRODUCTION

*S*irs," he said, "please don't go any further. Stop awhile and rest here in the shade of this tree while I get water to refresh your feet, and a bite to eat to strengthen you. Do stay awhile before continuing your journey."

Abraham, Genesis 18: 3–5, TLB

*W*hat's for dinner?" is the perennial, pesky question that draws you to this book. You might have tonight covered, but your family's need to eat—best yet eat together—comes in relentless waves.

And you have things to do besides cook! *Once-a-Month Cooking* is a method for people who don't always want to cook, but want to have cooked. You are smart and you understand that nothing unravels the seams of quality family time faster than having nothing on hand for dinner. Not having clean laundry runs a distant second.

Once-a-Month Cooking is a method of cooking a month's (or two weeks') dinner entrées at a time and freezing them. Yes, of course it works! (That's the question we're asked most often. Although a couple who cooks this way was featured in the *National Enquirer*, the method is not outrageous.)

You don't have to be particularly organized or a good cook to do this. You don't need a separate freezer. You don't need a Tupperware distributorship, although a drawerful of Tupperware will help.

We will take you by the hand and give you a shopping list and lots of direction. We'll tell you what size containers to freeze the food in and suggest what to serve with your entrées. When you're finished, gazing into your well-stocked freezer will be a near-spiritual experience. Afterward, on any given day you can cook from scratch if you want to, but if you don't have time—no problem. This is a great way to simplify your life, relieving it of the daily stress of what to fix for dinner.

The beauty of once-a-month cooking is that it provides the convenience of a home meal replacement—the restaurant industry's jargon for the take-out meal—with the aroma, appeal, taste, nutrition, and cost savings of home cooking. For the investment of one large grocery haul and a day of mega-cooking, you have a month's (or two weeks') entrées available on time each day with little effort on your part beyond putting an entrée into the oven and steaming vegetables or tossing a salad. And you won't need to dash in for fast food, Chinese takeout, or to the grocery store deli.

This system saves you money. Convenience foods are costly. So are forays into the supermarket at 5:00 P.M. with two preschoolers. A list that began with four items yields a cart holding twenty-two, including Fruit Loops and Big Chew gum. With once-a-month cooking you will have one large shopping trip a month (or two weeks), then shop perhaps once a week for fresh produce, breakfasts, and lunches.

A bonus from your day's cooking investment is your flexibility. Having guests is more fun when the main dish is ready in advance. Your family can carry on if you have surgery or a new baby, when the holidays approach, or if you are traveling. What a joy it is to be able to respond to special needs of your family and of others!

We all know that nutrition fares better when we aren't eating catch-as-catch-can. And if you or another family member are on a special diet, once-a-month cooking is an excellent way to feed the rest of the tribe.

You may want to try the two-week plan rather than a whole month if you are cooking in bulk for the first time or your family is small (fewer than four people). In that case two weeks' worth will last you at least three weeks if you package it in more, and smaller containers.

The greatest benefit of once-a-month cooking, however, is that it gives you a better shot at pulling the family together—at least a few evenings a week—to disengage from the concerns of the world and engage with one another. A warm meal on a set table wafts the aroma of care and value to a family. As one mom said, "When the food is ready, and we're gathered at the table, the rest of the craziness doesn't seem to matter."

Home meal replacements make it too easy for a family to separate, grab the meal when they want, and see to their own needs. *Once-a-Month Cooking* will help you have a meal to gather round. Share the kitchen chores as well as your mealtimes together.

Once we're at the table it's discouraging to fall into the same conversation ruts about work or teachers, or how a child has misbehaved today. With our own families and friends we've found it's helpful and fun to sometimes "put a question on the table." That is, ask a question that each person at the table must address, but for which there is no right or wrong answer, such as "What is the funniest thing you saw today?" "What is your favorite room of our home and why?" "If you were an animal rather than a person, what animal would you like to be?" We've included table talk questions to prime the pump for you. Turn off the television, ignore the telephone, and enjoy what you will learn about one another.

This cooking system was devised by Mimi to meet the daily needs of a busy family that had company often. In the years since then we have been encouraged and sometimes amused by the many uses people have found for—as we call it—"the method." Here are some that stretch beyond the obvious feeding of a busy family. Perhaps they will expand your vision for how you can use the wealth of food you will soon have on hand.

- Freeze individual portions to stock the freezer of an elderly parent or friend.
- Develop this as an at-home business to serve busy, two-income families. A day care provider uses *Once-a-Month Cooking* so that for a fee parents can pick up a dinner entrée with their child!
- Cook the method with friends in a church or community kitchen and use the entrées to take to families in crisis.
- For a baby gift or for a woman experiencing a difficult pregnancy, have the expectant mother purchase the groceries from the shopping list. The next day you come to her home, cook the entrées, and put them into her freezer.

We can't resist sharing our two personal favorite applications. On a visit to Peru, Mimi's husband, Calvin, a family physician, was part of a medical team that trekked into the jungle to treat a people group dying of pneumonia. When the team needed additional food, Mimi took frozen entrées, packaged in Tupperware and wrapped in newspapers, to a nearby airstrip. The pilot flew over the team's camp site in the jungle and dropped the entrées to them. We call this one "Bombs Away."

The final one involves a letter we received. We receive many letters (and phone calls on cooking day). Some users say the results have saved their marriages. One user said she actually accomplished cooking this way although her past cooking catastrophes had put a person in the hospital and included things like frying a chicken in Tide. This following letter is a favorite:

> Dear Madam,
>
> I ordered the book *Once-a-Month Cooking* . . . .
>
> As a bachelor, I have cooked in bulk for years, though my menu consists of only one or two items.
>
> I am interested in mail order bulk food distributors. Do you have some addresses I could try?
>
> Thanks for your time,
> Dave Listoe
> North Pole, Alaska

Whatever your impulse for trying *Once-a-Month Cooking,* we trust you'll find generous rewards for your day's cooking.

If you have used a previous edition of *Once-a-Month Cooking*, you will find in this edition a new two-week cycle of recipes, a few recipe substitutions in the other menu cycles, and a general fine-tuning. You will also see that one two-week plan, chapter two, is a condensed version of a one-month cycle, so its recipes appear both places.

Are you ready to win the race to have meals on hand? On your mark. Get set. Let the adventure begin!

CHAPTER ONE
Cooking the Once-a-Month Way

*C*heerfully share your home
with those who need a meal or a
place to stay for the night.

1 Peter 4:9, TLB

WARMING UP: AN OVERVIEW OF THE ONCE-A-MONTH PLAN

*T*his cooking method enables you to prepare either a month or two weeks' main dishes at once and freeze them. The book includes two choices of one-month cycles and three choices of two-week cycles. If you rotate among these, you can easily provide great mealtime variety. We suggest that you start with a cycle from the book to get used to the method. Then you can experiment with adding favorite family recipes. Turn to chapter 9 for help in adapting the method to your own recipes.

Each menu cycle gives you a menu calendar that shows the month's entrées at a glance, a grocery shopping list, a list of staples that the menu cycle assumes you have on hand (so you can buy any you don't have), a list of the containers you will need for freezing the entrées, step-by-step instructions for preparing the recipes in sequence on your cooking day, and finally the recipes themselves in the order you will prepare them.

To serve an entrée, you will need to thaw the dish and heat it. Meanwhile you can turn your attention to preparing a vegetable, salad, or perhaps a dessert to serve with it. The time-consuming preparation and cleanup is done all at once on your mega-cooking day!

Since many of the entrées can be frozen in freezer bags instead of bulkier hard-sided containers, even a month's cycle can be stored in the freezer accompanying your refrigerator. If you are using your refrigerator's freezer, you will need to make room in it by cleaning it out before your cooking day. (Sooner or later you would need to deal with those hard knots of leftovers anyway!) Right after cooking day you will not have room in the refrigerator's freezer for things like ice cream and loaves of bread, but as you use entrées from the freezer you can add these to it.

The recipes in *Once-a-Month Cooking* don't come from stainless-steel test kitchens, but have been tested numerous times in homes by cooks of various cooking abilities. We have selected recipes we think your family will eat and enjoy. They were chosen for taste, variety, nutritional value, easily available ingredients, and how well they lend themselves to freezing.

One of the two-week cycles consists entirely of low-fat entrées, selected in consultation with a dietitian. With the other menu cycles you may adjust as you like for low-fat, for example, using soups and dairy products with reduced fat content.

You will find that the recipes vary in serving size. The average is five or six servings. Some serve four; a few serve twelve. Depending upon the ages (and eating habits) of your children, if you have four or fewer family members, you may want to divide and freeze each larger-serving entrée in two or more meal-size portions. The largest recipes are great for serving company or ensuring leftovers the following day.

You may find that a month menu cycle actually feeds your family for five weeks or six or more—particularly if you occasionally eat out or supplement your menu with dinner salads or easy meals like grilled meats and vegetables.

In chapter 8 you will find a few of our favorite bread, breakfast, dessert, salad, and vegetable recipes to serve with your entrées.

Consult chapter 10 for helpful information on such things as freezing tips and food measurement equivalents.

AT THE STARTING LINE

Are you ready to cook? Or at least ready to *think* about getting ready to cook? Let us provide some tips to streamline the process.

First, read this introductory material. Then choose which menu cycle you would like to try this month and read through that chapter so you'll know what's ahead.

Next comes the hardest part: crossing off the time on your calendar to grocery shop and cook. But if you don't do this, you won't accomplish once-a-month cooking. These should be on adjacent days. Don't try to shop and cook on the same day, especially if you have young children, or you won't like us very much! You simply won't have the time or energy to do both. You might also not like us about four hours into your cooking day, when your feet are complaining and every pot and pan you own is dirty. But we are consoled by the thought that you will like us *very much* when you peek at your larder, carefully labeled and layered in your freezer, as well as each day thereafter at about 5:00 P.M. The month cycles require about (of course this varies with the cook) a nine-hour day. The two-week cycles take about four to five hours.

Cook with a friend or your spouse or an older child. The day goes so much more quickly when you divide the work and add the conversation. If you have young children, a cooking companion can help tend the kids, answer the phone, and wipe the counters. You can either divide up the food or cook one day a month at your friend's home and one day a month at your own.

Trust us that you will want to go out to dinner on cooking day. Yes, we know you will have plenty on hand for dinner, but you won't want to face any of it on your plate. This will pass. Go out, then have your spouse and kids wash the dishes.

Err to the side of buying a little more produce, chicken, and ground beef than is called for on your shopping lists. You can always use these for salads, soups, and sandwiches. If you have chicken broth left over, freeze it in an ice cube tray. When the cubes are frozen, pop them into a freezer bag. You can pull out a cube when a recipe calls for chicken broth, or make spur-of-the-moment chicken soup with leftovers.

You may want to photocopy the recipes and attach them to large index cards. In many cases you will be working on more than one recipe at a time. You can lay out your recipe cards in sequence to save you from having to keep turning the pages.

Don't even think about trying to do extra baking on your cooking day. If you enjoy making pie crust and want to use your own rather than a store-bought one, prepare the pie crust a couple of days ahead.

Finally, although you need to free yourself of commitments on your cooking day, the day will go much easier if you feel free to take a break to tend to the children's needs, make a phone call, or just sit down and rest! Wear supportive shoes. Listen to your favorite music. Crack open a kitchen window for ventilation and to let the good smells pour out.

The secret of the method involves *doing all similar processes at once:* browning ground beef and chopping onions and cooking chicken only once rather than several times a month. Imagine the hours this saves!

GROCERY SHOPPING HINTS

Before you go to the supermarket, read the grocery and staples lists for the menu cycle you plan to use. The staples list contains items you need but probably have on hand. Look through your cupboards and add the missing staple items to the grocery shopping list. Also check the list of suggested freezer containers to see if you need to buy any of them.

For added convenience, use a copier to reproduce the grocery list; then write in the other staple items or containers you'll need to buy. The grocery lists have been categorized by sections of food to help speed you through the store.

If you shop for a month menu cycle, you will have to push one cart and pull another. You may need to budget more carefully in order to set aside the funds needed to purchase food for all your dinner entrées at once. But keep in mind that over the course of the month you will save money on your food bill by cooking this way because you'll be buying in bulk, eating out less often, and eliminating unplanned trips to the supermarket.

Your shopping trip will take you a couple of hours, so don't try to wedge it between two appointments. If you take young children, be sure to go when everyone is well-fed and rested. It also helps to break up the trip. For example, go mid-morning to a discount food store to buy in bulk, have lunch at a favorite spot, and then finish any leftover shopping at the supermarket. If a friend or relative can baby-sit for you on shopping day, you will accomplish more in less time.

When you get home from shopping, you don't have to put everything away. Stack the canned goods and dry ingredients on a table or counter because you'll be using them soon. Keeping them within sight can inspire you for the task ahead!

The grocery shopping lists include some items with asterisks(*). These can be stored because you will not need them until the day you serve the corresponding entrée. Mark the labels of these items to remind you not to use them by mistake. For example, place an X in marker across a soup label, a package of rice or spaghetti, or on a plastic bag holding a fresh tomato.

THE DAY BEFORE COOKING DAY

After you've returned from the grocery store, clear off the kitchen counters, removing any appliances you won't be using. Create as much free countertop space as you can. Then, following the "Equipment Needed for Cooking Day" list, pull out your food processor, mixer, bowls—the tools you will need. If you have room, you may also want to get out the staple items.

Make sure you have all needed groceries on hand. Then perform the tasks that your chosen menu cycle outlines for the day before cooking day.

If you don't have a food processor to chop and slice the vegetables, you may want to cut them up the day before cooking since this is one of the most time-consuming tasks. Then store these vegetables in the refrigerator in cold water, inside tightly sealed plastic containers, or omit the water and seal them in zip-closure bags. (Do not store mushrooms in water.)

Finally, check the list of freezer containers needed for the entrées in your menu cycle and get out the ones you'll need. You can usually store entrées in freezer bags unless they are layered, like lasagna, or contain a lot of liquid. Food stored in freezer bags can be thawed in the bag and then warmed in a suitable container.

COOKING DAY

The assembly order for each menu cycle is a step-by-step guide to preparing all your entrées. Read through the assembly order before you start to cook. Since you will usually be working on more than one recipe at a time, getting an overview will give you a sense of how the steps flow together.

The following suggestions will help make this method work best for you:

❊ Place an empty trash can in the center of the kitchen, and corral the pets where they won't be underfoot. You'll want to avoid wasted motion wherever possible on cooking day.

❊ Use a timer—or two timers when necessary—to remind you something is in the oven or boiling for a certain length of time.

❊ Pause to wash pots and pans as necessary. Washing dishes and wiping up periodically as you work will help you work more efficiently and make end-of-the-day cleanup easier.

❊ If you sauté several food items in succession, use the same skillet. Sometimes you'll only need to wipe it out and put in the next ingredients. Put a slow cooker to work by using it overnight for brisket, for example, and then for soup or stew on cooking day.

❊ Set frequently used spices along the back of the stove or on a nearby counter. Use one set of measuring cups and spoons for wet ingredients and another for dry. That way you'll need to wash them less often.

❊ You will *perform all similar tasks at once*. For example, grate, chop, and slice all the carrots, celery, cheese, and onions. Set them aside in separate bowls or plastic bags. Cook all the chicken if you didn't do that the day before. Brown all the ground beef and sauté all the onions at one time. These tasks may seem tedious, but you will have accomplished a lot when you're finished, and assembling the dishes will go much faster.

❊ Whenever a chicken recipe doesn't specifically call for cooked chicken in the ingredients list, it means you will use raw chicken.

❊ At the close of your cooking day, save leftover sliced or diced vegetables and cooked meat for a soup, a salad, or for snacks.

FOOD STORAGE AND FREEZER TIPS

As you complete recipes, set them aside on a table to cool enough so they won't heat up the other foods in your freezer. When one or two have cooled, label each with the name of the entrée, the date you prepared it, and cooking instructions, so you won't have to consult the recipe when you are preparing to serve it. For example:

Aztec Quiche

10/8

Bake uncov. 40–50 mins. at 325 degrees

If a recipe calls for cheese to be sprinkled on top the last few minutes of baking, pour the grated cheese in a small freezer bag. Tape the bag to the side or top of the corresponding entrée's container so that you are freezing the two together.

Make the best use of your 13x9x2-inch baking dishes. Spray a dish with nonstick spray, line the dish with heavy aluminum foil, seal the entrée, and freeze it. When the entrée has frozen completely, remove it in the foil and return it to the freezer, thereby freeing your dish to be used for something else.

When sealing food for freezing, remove as much air from the container as possible, and seal it airtight. That will help guard against the cardboard-like taste called "freezer burn." When using freezer bags, label the bag with an indelible marker before you insert the food.

Post the menu of foods you've prepared on your freezer or inside a cupboard door to help you choose each day's dinner and to keep an inventory of what entrées you've used. Check off the dishes as you serve them. For the freshest taste, seal containers airtight and use them within a month to six weeks. (For additional freezer storage tips, see chapter 10.)

SERVING SUGGESTIONS

Remember each evening to pull the next night's entrée from the freezer and put it in the refrigerator to thaw. If the food is in a freezer bag, set the bag in a casserole dish to thaw, in case any liquid leaks out. You can also thaw the dish in the microwave the next day. If the entrée is sealed securely in a freezer bag, you can thaw it in cold water. We don't recommend that you thaw food on the counter because of the danger of spoilage if it sits out too long after it is thawed.

Each recipe includes suggestions for salads or vegetables you might serve with the entrée. You'll find some of those recipes in chapter 8. Now that you've saved time on your entrées, try some new salads, vegetables, or desserts, whether you'll have company or the same familiar faces around your table.

You'll spend less time in the kitchen during the coming weeks. You will save time, money, and energy that you can invest in many other ways. Imagine how good it will feel to have entrées on hand, and to have an immediate answer to each day's nagging question: "What's for dinner?"

Let's get cooking!

EQUIPMENT NEEDED FOR COOKING DAY

On cooking day, you'll want to reuse bowls and pans as much as possible to conserve counter and stove-top space. The following equipment will be needed:

APPLIANCES

blender or hand mixer (one-month A plan)
Crockpot (one-month A and B plans)
food processor or grater

POTS, PANS, AND SKILLETS

1 extra large pot, canning kettle, or 2 large pots
1 large saucepan with lid
1 medium saucepan with lid
1 small saucepan
1 large skillet
1 medium skillet
1 rimmed baking sheet (two-week A plan, one-month B plan); 2 rimmed baking sheets
    (low-fat plan)

BOWLS AND CONTAINERS

1 set of large, medium, and small mixing bowls
8 to 12 small-to-medium bowls or plastic bags (for grated, sliced, or chopped ingredients)

MISCELLANEOUS TOOLS

can opener
colander
cutting board
hot pads

CHAPTER ONE

kitchen scissors

knives (cutting and paring)

ladle

2 sets of measuring cups (one for wet ingredients and one for dry)

2 sets of measuring spoons (one for wet ingredients and one for dry)

masking tape or labels

metal or plastic serving spatula

mixing spoons

rolling pin

rubber gloves (for deboning chicken and mixing food)

rubber spatula

tongs

vegetable peeler

waterproof marking pen

wire whisk

CHAPTER TWO

Two-Week Entrée Plan A

*F*or God, who gives seed to
the farmer to plant, and later on,
good crops to harvest and eat,
will give you more and more
seed to plant and will make
it grow so that you can give
away more and more fruit
from your harvest.

2 Corinthians 9:10, TLB

ONCE-A-MONTH COOKING

Menu
· C A L E N D A R ·

Sunday	Monday	Tuesday	Wednesday	Thursday	Friday	Saturday
	Eat Out Cooking Day! 1	Chicken Packets 2	Mexican Stroganoff 3	French Bread Pizza 4	Calzones 5	Chili Verde 6
Spaghetti 7	Wild Rice Chicken 8	Balkan Meatballs 9	Marinated Flank Steak 10	Chicken Broccoli 11	Linguine à la Anne 12	Chili Hamburgers 13
Baked Eggs 14	Poulet de France 15	16	17	18	19	20
21	22	23	24	25	26	27
28	29	30				

CHAPTER TWO

GROCERY SHOPPING AND STAPLES LISTS

An asterisk (*) after an item indicates it can be stored until you cook the dish it will be served with. For example, the spaghetti noodles will not be cooked until the day you serve Spaghetti. Mark those items as a reminder that you will need them for an entrée.

When entrées require perishable foods to be refrigerated until served, you may want to use those dishes right away or buy the food the week you plan to prepare the dish. For example, fresh mushrooms would spoil by the end of a month.

For two-week entrée plan A, you will need these food items as well as the ones in the staples list that follows.

GROCERY SHOPPING LIST

Canned Goods

1 4-ounce can chopped, green chilies

2 10¾-ounce cans condensed cream of mushroom soup

1 10¾-ounce can condensed cream of chicken soup

1 12-ounce can evaporated skim milk

1 8-ounce and 2 4-ounce cans mushroom stems and pieces

1 11½-ounce jar salsa*

3 28-ounce cans Italian-style or plain crushed tomatoes in puree

1 12-ounce can tomato paste

1 8-ounce can sliced water chestnuts

Grains, Noodles, and Rice

4 hamburger buns

6 bread slices

1 loaf unsliced French bread (not sourdough)*

2 cups (approx.) seasoned croutons (1 cup croutons, ½ cup and ⅓ cup crushed crouton crumbs)

1 12-ounce package linguine

1 dozen corn tortillas*

1 8-ounce and 1 12-ounce package wide egg noodles*

8 ounces (1¼ cups) dry pinto beans

1 16-ounce package spaghetti*

1 12-ounce package seasoned bread stuffing—7-pound bird size (6 cups)

1 6¼-ounce package long grain and wild rice (Uncle Ben's Fast Cooking Long Grain and Wild Rice if available)

Frozen Foods

1 10-ounce package frozen, chopped broccoli

2 loaves frozen bread dough (Italian or French if available, otherwise wheat)

Dairy Products

9 eggs

¾ cup margarine

10 ounces (2½ cups) grated, mild cheddar cheese

10 ounces (2½ cups; 1 cup will be saved*) grated mozzarella cheese

4 ounces (1 cup) grated, low-fat Monterey Jack cheese*

4 ounces (1 cup) grated Parmesan cheese

2 ounces (½ cup) Romano cheese

1 3-ounce package cream cheese

1 8-ounce carton sour cream or low-fat yogurt*

2 8-ounce packages refrigerated crescent rolls*

7 cups milk

Meat and Poultry

10 pounds whole chicken or 8 pounds chicken breasts

1 pound boneless, skinless chicken breasts

1⅔ pounds cooked ham

2 pounds lean ground beef (or substitute ground turkey)

1 pound bulk Italian sausage

1⅓ pounds flank steak

½ of a 3-ounce package of sliced pepperoni*

2 pounds round steak

½ pound ground turkey

Produce

    1 small bunch celery
    8 cloves garlic
    1½ pounds brown or yellow onions
    1 bunch fresh parsley
    2 green bell peppers and 1 red bell pepper (or 3 green bell peppers)

STAPLES LIST

Make sure you have the following staples on hand; add those you don't have to the above shopping list:

    ground allspice
    dried basil leaves
    bay leaves (4)
    black pepper
    cayenne pepper
    chili powder (2 tablespoons)
    chili sauce (½ cup plus 1 tablespoon)
    chopped chives (¼ cup plus 1 tablespoon)
    ground cloves
    ground cumin
    curry powder
    all-purpose flour (¼ cup plus 1 tablespoon)
    ground ginger
    light mayonnaise (2 cups)
    minced onion
    nonstick spray
    ground nutmeg
    dried oregano leaves
    paprika
    red wine vinegar (about ¾ cup)
    salt
    seasoned salt
    soy sauce (¼ cup plus 1 teaspoon)

sugar

vegetable oil (1 cup)

waxed paper

Worcestershire sauce (2 teaspoons)

FREEZER CONTAINERS

The following list of freezer containers or flat baking dishes will be needed for the entrées in two-week cycle A. They're not the only containers in which you could freeze these foods, but the list gives you an idea of the size and number of containers you'll need.

10 sandwich bags:
Calzones

11 1-quart freezer bags:
Chicken Packets (2), French Bread Pizza (3), Poulet de France, Linguine à la Anne (2), Calzones (2), Chili Verde

6 1-gallon freezer bags:
Wild Rice Chicken, Calzones (2), Balkan Meatballs, Chili Hamburgers, Marinated Flank Steak

1 3-cup container:
French Bread Pizza

1 4-cup container:
Spaghetti Sauce

1 5-cup container:
Chili Verde

1 6-cup container:
Mexican Stroganoff

3 13x9x2-inch baking dishes:
Poulet de France, Baked Eggs, Linguine à la Anne

1 7x11x2-inch baking dish:
Chicken Broccoli

Heavy aluminum foil
French Bread Pizza

THE DAY BEFORE COOKING DAY

1. Freeze the 4 hamburger buns in a plastic bag and the French bread in heavy foil, with the package of pepperoni taped to the foil. Refrigerate crescent rolls.

2. Cut 1 pound of boneless, skinless chicken breasts into 1-inch cubes with kitchen scissors for Chili Verdes; refrigerate until needed.

3. In a large pot (may need two), place the 10 pounds of whole chickens (or 8 pounds of breasts) in about 3 quarts water, making sure they're completely covered. Heat to a boil; reduce heat. Cover and simmer until thickest pieces are done, about 45 minutes to 1 hour. Save and refrigerate 6⅓ cups chicken broth; discard remaining broth or use for soup.

   Cool chicken until ready to handle; remove skin and debone. Cut into bite-size pieces with kitchen scissors, which are easier to use than a knife. Refrigerate chicken pieces in two plastic bags.

4. Set out appliances, bowls, canned goods, dry ingredients, freezer containers, and recipes.

5. Thaw 2 loaves of frozen baking dough in the refrigerator overnight.

6. Rinse pinto beans; cover with water and soak overnight.

COOKING DAY ASSEMBLY ORDER

   Make sure you've cleared the table and counters of unnecessary kitchenware to allow plenty of working room. It also helps to have fresh, damp washcloths and towels for wiping your hands and the cooking area. The day will go a lot smoother if you clean and organize as you work.

   Before you prepare a recipe, gather all the spices and ingredients in the assembly area to save time and steps. When you finish the recipe, remove unneeded items and wipe off the work space.

   Slightly undercook regular rice and noodles (al dente) that will be frozen. When you reheat them, they'll have a better consistency and won't turn mushy.

BEFORE ASSEMBLING DISHES

1. Cook and stir the bulk Italian sausage until brown in a large pot for Spaghetti Sauce. Take a minute after chopping the onions, garlic, and parsley to complete Spaghetti Sauce according to recipe. Start sauce boiling on the front burner, reduce heat, and then move pan to a back burner for 2 hours of simmering.

2. Perform all the chopping, grating, and slicing tasks.
>   Onions: finely chop all (store in cold water in a container with a tight-fitting lid).
>   Garlic: mince 8 cloves.
>   Parsley: chop ½ cup.
>   Celery: finely chop 1½ cups.
>   Green and red bell peppers: chop ¼ cup plus 1 tablespoon green bell pepper; slice 1
>   green and 1 red pepper.
>   Cheddar cheese: grate all.
>   Monterey Jack cheese: grate all.
>   Mozzarella cheese: grate 4 ounces; slice 6 ounces.
>   Croutons: crush enough to make 1 cup crumbs.

3. Spray pans or baking dishes you will need with nonstick spray (check list of freezer containers on page 22).

4. As you assemble the chicken, ham, beef, and miscellaneous entrées, allow them to cool if necessary, put them in storage containers, and freeze them.

ASSEMBLE CHICKEN DISHES

1. Skim off and discard chicken fat from 6⅓ cups chicken broth.

2. Start the Chili Verde.

3. Cook rice for Wild Rice Chicken according to package directions.

4. Make filling for Chicken Packets in a medium bowl (mixing with hands works best), put mixture in a bag, and freeze.

5. Assemble Wild Rice Chicken.

6. Start Poulet de France.

7. Start cooking 10-ounce package of frozen, chopped broccoli.

8. Finish assembling Poulet de France.

9. Assemble Chicken Broccoli.

10. Add chicken and spices to Chili Verde, and simmer 10 more minutes.

11. Cool Spaghetti Sauce, and freeze as directed.

12. Freeze chicken dishes.

ASSEMBLE HAM DISHES

1. Dice 1⅔ pounds ham, placing 4 cups in one bowl and 1 cup in another.

2. Boil linguine according to package directions.

3. Assemble Baked Eggs.

4. Complete Linguine à la Anne.

5. Freeze ham dishes.

ASSEMBLE BEEF DISHES

1. Prepare Calzones and freeze.

2. Cut round steak in bite-size pieces.

3. Combine ingredients for Mexican Stroganoff, and start it simmering.

4. Assemble and broil Balkan Meatballs.

5. Prepare Marinated Flank Steak.

6. Prepare Chili Hamburger patties.

7. Freeze beef dishes.

COOKING DAY ASSEMBLY ORDER

RECIPES FOR TWO-WEEK ENTRÉE PLAN A

Each recipe offers complete instructions on how to prepare the dish. Food items with an asterisk (*) won't be prepared until you serve the entrée. For recipes calling for oven baking, preheat oven for about 10 minutes.

"Summary of processes" gives a quick overview of foods that need to be chopped, diced, grated, or sliced. "Freeze in" tells what bags and containers will be needed to freeze each entrée. "Serve with" offers suggestions of foods to accompany the meal. Some of the recipes for those foods are included in chapter 8; page numbers are indicated for easy reference. "Note" includes special instructions on how the entrée can be used in other ways.

SPAGHETTI SAUCE

1 pound bulk Italian sausage
1½ cups finely chopped onion
1 12-ounce can tomato paste
3 28-ounce cans Italian-style or plain crushed tomatoes in puree
2 cups water
4 teaspoons minced garlic (4 cloves)
4 bay leaves
2 tablespoons sugar
4 teaspoons dried basil leaves
2 teaspoons dried oregano leaves
4 tablespoons chopped fresh parsley
2 teaspoons salt
1 16-ounce package spaghetti*

*I*n a large pot, cook and stir the bulk Italian sausage with the onion until the meat is brown; drain fat. Add remaining ingredients, except the spaghetti. Bring sauce to a boil; reduce heat. Partly cover, and simmer for 2 hours, stirring occasionally. (If desired, simmer in a Crockpot instead of pot.) Makes 12 cups sauce.

After sauce has cooled, freeze 4 cups for Spaghetti and 3 cups for French Bread Pizza; divide remaining 5 cups sauce in half, and freeze in 2 1-quart bags for Calzones.

To prepare for serving Spaghetti, thaw sauce, and heat in a medium saucepan. Cook noodles according to package directions, drain, and pour sauce over them. Makes 6 servings.

Summary of processes: Chop 1½ cups onion, 4 tablespoons parsley; mince 4 cloves garlic

Freeze in: 4-cup container, Spaghetti; 3-cup container, French Bread Pizza; 2 1-quart freezer bags, Calzones

Serve with: Fresh Baked Asparagus (page 200), Cheesy-Herb Bread (page 180)

RECIPES

FRENCH BREAD PIZZA

1 loaf unsliced French bread (not sourdough)*
3 cups Spaghetti Sauce*
¼ cup grated Parmesan cheese*
1 cup grated mozzarella cheese*
3 ounces pepperoni slices (half a package)*

*T*his recipe is assembled on the day it's served. Put sauce in a 3-cup container, cheeses in 2 1-quart bags, and pepperoni in 1-quart bag; wrap bread in heavy foil. Freeze them together.

To prepare for serving, thaw French bread, sauce, grated cheeses, and pepperoni. Set oven to broil and/or 550°. Slice loaf of French bread in half lengthwise. Layer sauce, Parmesan cheese, pepperoni, and mozzarella cheese on each half. Place bread on baking sheet, and put in oven. Broil until mozzarella is melted. Cut pizza into serving-size pieces. Makes 6 to 8 servings.

Summary of processes: Grate 4 ounces mozzarella cheese

Freeze in: 3-cup container; 3 1-quart bags; foil for bread

Serve with: Waldorf salad

CHILI VERDE

8 ounces dry pinto beans (1¼ cups)
1 pound boneless, skinless chicken breasts
1 4-ounce can chopped green chilies
1 teaspoon ground cumin
¾ teaspoon dried oregano leaves
⅛ teaspoon ground cloves
⅛ teaspoon cayenne pepper
3 cups chicken broth
1 teaspoon minced garlic (1 clove)
1 teaspoon salt
⅔ cup finely chopped onion
1 cup grated low-fat Monterey Jack cheese*
1 dozen corn tortillas*
1 11½-ounce jar salsa*

*R*inse pinto beans, soak them in cold water overnight, then drain. Cut chicken into 1-inch cubes; cook until no longer pink in small amount of water. Combine chicken with chilies and seasonings; refrigerate until needed. At the same time, combine beans, chicken broth, garlic, salt, and onion in a large pot; bring to a boil. Reduce heat and simmer until beans are soft, about 1 hour. Add more water if necessary.

Combine chicken and spices with beans; simmer 10 more minutes. Cool and freeze. Grate cheese, put in a 1-quart bag, and attach it to the freezer container with the chili.

To serve, thaw chili and cheese. Simmer chili 30 minutes, stirring occasionally. Top chili with salsa and grated cheese; serve on warmed corn tortillas. Makes 5 servings.

Summary of processes: Soak ½ pound pinto beans overnight; cut 1 pound boneless chicken into cubes; finely chop ⅔ cup onion; grate 1 cup low-fat Monterey Jack cheese

Freeze in: 5-cup container; 1-quart bag

Serve with: Tossed green salad

WILD RICE CHICKEN

1 6¼-ounce package quick-cooking long grain and wild rice
1 cup cooked, chopped chicken
1 8-ounce can sliced water chestnuts, drained
1 cup finely chopped celery
1¼ cups finely chopped onion
1 cup light mayonnaise*
1 10¾-ounce can condensed cream of mushroom soup*

*C*ook rice according to package directions. Combine rice with chopped chicken, water chestnuts, celery, and onion; put mixture in a 1-gallon freezer bag.

To prepare for serving, thaw rice and chicken mixture, remove from bag, and place in a 2½-quart baking dish that has been sprayed with nonstick spray. Preheat oven to 325°. Stir mayonnaise and condensed cream of mushroom soup together, and spread over top of chicken. Cover and bake for 1 hour. Makes 6 servings.

Summary of processes: Chop 1 cup cooked chicken, 1 cup celery, and 1¼ cups onion

Freeze in: 1-gallon bag

Serve with: Cooked green beans, peach halves with cottage cheese topped with a maraschino cherry, and Blueberry Pie (page 192)

CHICKEN PACKETS

2 cups cooked, chopped chicken
1 3-ounce package cream cheese, softened
1 tablespoon chopped chives
2 tablespoons milk
Salt to taste
½ cup crushed, seasoned crouton crumbs*
2 8-ounce packages refrigerated crescent rolls*
¼ cup (½ stick) melted margarine*

*M*ix chicken, cream cheese, chives, milk, and salt in a medium bowl (mixing with hands works best) to make filling, and store in a 1-quart freezer bag. Put crouton crumbs in another 1-quart bag, attach it to bag of chicken filling, and freeze. Refrigerate crescent rolls.

To prepare for serving, thaw chicken mixture. Preheat oven to 350°. Unroll crescent rolls. Each tube will contain 4 rectangles of dough with a diagonal perforation. Press dough along each perforation so the rectangle halves will not separate. Place about ¼ cup of chicken mixture into the center of each rectangle. Fold dough over the filling, and pinch the edges to seal tightly. Dip each packet in melted margarine, and coat with crouton crumbs. Place packets on a baking sheet. Bake for 20 minutes or until golden brown. Packets are good either hot or cold. (Serve early in the month before date expires on crescent rolls.) Makes 8 packets.

Summary of processes: Chop 2 cups cooked chicken and 1 tablespoon chives

Freeze in: 2 1-quart bags

Serve with: Smoky Corn Chowder (page 198), baked apples stuffed with plump raisins

Note: These packets are a favorite with children.

POULET DE FRANCE

1 12-ounce package seasoned bread stuffing (6 cups)
2 tablespoons melted margarine
2 cups chicken broth, divided
3 cups chopped, cooked chicken
½ cup finely chopped onion
¼ cup minced chives
½ cup finely chopped celery
½ cup light mayonnaise
¾ teaspoon salt
2 eggs
1½ cups milk
1 10¾-ounce can condensed cream of mushroom soup
½ cup grated mild cheddar cheese

*I*n a medium bowl, mix stuffing, melted margarine, and 1¼ cups broth. Mix chicken, ¾ cup broth, onion, chives, celery, mayonnaise, and salt in another bowl.

Spread half the stuffing in a 13x9x2-inch baking dish treated with nonstick spray. Spread chicken mixture over stuffing. Cover with remaining stuffing. Whisk eggs, milk, and soup in a large bowl. Pour sauce evenly over stuffing. Cover dish with foil, and freeze. Put cheese in a small freezer bag, and attach it to dish.

To prepare for serving, thaw grated cheese and chicken dish. Preheat oven to 325°. Cover and bake for 30 minutes. Remove foil, sprinkle with cheese, and continue to bake, uncovered, for 10 minutes more. Makes 8 servings.

Summary of processes: Chop 3 cups cooked chicken, ½ cup onion, and ½ cup celery; mince ¼ cup chives; grate ½ cup mild cheddar cheese

Freeze in: 13x9x2-inch baking dish; 1-quart bag

Serve with: Cooked frozen peas, lemon gelatin with pears, Cranberry Tea (page 191)

Note: This is a super dish to take to a potluck dinner.

CHICKEN BROCCOLI

1 10-ounce package frozen, chopped broccoli
4 cups cooked, chopped chicken
1 10¾-ounce can condensed cream of chicken soup
½ cup light mayonnaise
1 4-ounce can mushroom stems and pieces, drained
¼ teaspoon curry powder
¾ cup grated Parmesan cheese, divided

*C*ook broccoli in boiling water according to package directions. Drain broccoli, and spread it in a 7x11x2-inch baking dish treated with nonstick spray. Mix chicken, soup, mayonnaise, mushrooms, curry powder, and ½ cup Parmesan cheese in a medium bowl. Spread chicken mixture over broccoli. Sprinkle ¼ cup Parmesan cheese over top. Cover dish with foil, and freeze.

To prepare for serving, thaw dish. Preheat oven to 350°. Cover and bake for 40 minutes. Remove foil, stir to bring colder food in center to the outside; bake 20 minutes more. Makes 6 servings.

Summary of processes: Chop 4 cups cooked chicken

Freeze in: 7x11x2-inch baking dish

Serve with: Croissants, Cranberry Cream Salad (page 196)

RECIPES

BAKED EGGS

6 bread slices, cut in cubes
2 cups grated mild cheddar cheese
1 cup cooked, cubed ham
¼ cup chopped green bell pepper
½ cup finely chopped onion
6 eggs
3 cups milk

*M*ix bread, cheese, ham, bell pepper, and onion; spread in a 13x9x2-inch baking dish treated with nonstick spray. Whisk eggs and milk together, and pour over top. Cover dish with foil and freeze.

To prepare for serving, thaw dish, and preheat oven to 375°. Bake, uncovered, for 45 minutes. Makes 8 to 10 servings.

Summary of processes: Cut bread and ham into cubes; grate 2 cups mild cheddar cheese; chop ¼ cup green bell pepper and ½ cup onion

Freeze in: 13x9x2-inch baking dish

Serve with: Hot Spiced Fruit (page 198)

Note: This dish is good with 6 slices cooked, crumbled bacon instead of ham. You can also make this dish the night before, refrigerate it, and serve it the next morning. It's nice for company brunch after church.

CHAPTER TWO

LINGUINE À LA ANNE

1 12-ounce package linguine
2 tablespoons margarine
2 tablespoons all-purpose flour
½ teaspoon salt
1 12-ounce can evaporated skim milk
1 4-ounce can mushroom stems and pieces, save liquid
1⅓ cups chicken broth
4 cups cooked, cubed ham
½ cup grated Romano cheese
1 sliced red bell pepper
1 sliced green bell pepper
1 tablespoon vegetable oil
1 cup seasoned croutons*

*C*ook linguine in a large pot according to package directions, drain, and return to pot. While linguine cooks, melt margarine in a medium saucepan over low heat. Stir in flour and salt, adding evaporated milk. Bring to a boil, stirring constantly. Boil and stir 1 minute. Add liquid from mushrooms and the chicken broth. Cook over medium heat, stirring constantly until bubbly and slightly thickened.

Add 2 cups sauce and drained mushrooms to linguine; toss until well mixed. Spoon linguine mixture into a 13x9x2-inch baking dish that has been treated with nonstick spray, pressing the linguine mixture up the sides to leave a slight hollow in center of dish.

Toss ham in remaining sauce; spread it in the center of the linguine. Sprinkle with Romano cheese, cover with foil, and freeze dish. Sauté red and green bell peppers in vegetable oil until soft; allow to cool. Put peppers in 1-quart freezer bag; attach this bag and croutons in a 1-quart freezer bag to the dish.

To prepare for serving, thaw dish, peppers, and croutons. Preheat oven to 400°. Bake dish, uncovered, for 20 minutes. Before serving, sprinkle croutons around edge of casserole. Reheat sautéed red and green bell peppers, and mound them in the center. Makes 8 servings.

Summary of processes: Cut ham into cubes; slice 1 red bell pepper and 1 green bell pepper

Freeze in: 13x9x2-inch baking dish; 2 1-quart bags

Serve with: Cooked zucchini, Orange Spiced Tea (page 191)

Note: Great for company that includes children.

CALZONES

2 loaves frozen bread dough (Italian, French, or white)
6 ounces grated mozzarella cheese
5 cups Spaghetti Sauce

*T*haw two loaves of bread dough. Divide each loaf into 5 parts. One at a time, roll each dough piece on a floured board or stretch with your hands, making 10 7-inch squares. Fold each dough square over a pinch of cheese to form a turnover, and pinch edges to seal.

Place each turnover in a small sandwich bag. Put 5 turnovers in a 1-gallon freezer bag. Divide sauce in half, and store in 2 1-quart freezer bags; enclose each bag of sauce in a bag of Calzones. Do the same with the remaining 5 turnovers.

To prepare for serving, thaw sauce; heat in a medium pan 10 to 15 minutes until bubbly. At the same time, take frozen turnovers out of bags, and place them about 2 inches apart on a baking sheet sprayed with nonstick spray. Preheat oven to 350°. Bake for about 20 minutes. Turnovers will be golden brown when done. Ladle sauce on top of turnovers and serve. Makes 10 servings.

Freeze in: 2 1-gallon bags; 2 1-quart bags; 10 sandwich bags

Serve with: Tossed salad with Italian dressing

Note: All ages love these! They're convenient, since you can bake only as many as are needed at a time. Reheat for lunches.

MEXICAN STROGANOFF

2 pounds round steak
1 cup finely chopped onion
2 teaspoons minced garlic (2 cloves)
2 tablespoons vegetable oil
⅓ cup red wine vinegar
1¾ cups water
½ cup chili sauce
1 tablespoon paprika
1 tablespoon chili powder
2 teaspoons seasoned salt
1 teaspoon soy sauce
1 8-ounce can mushroom stems and pieces, drained
1 12-ounce package wide egg noodles*
1 8-ounce carton sour cream or low-fat yogurt*
3 tablespoons all-purpose flour*

*C*ut steak into bite-size pieces. Cook and stir steak, onion, and garlic in oil in a large saucepan over medium heat until brown. Drain off oil. Stir vinegar, water, chili sauce, paprika, chili powder, seasoned salt, soy sauce, and mushrooms into steak mixture. Bring to a boil; reduce heat. Cover and simmer 1 hour until meat is tender. Cool and store in freezer container.

To prepare for serving, thaw meat mixture and heat in saucepan until bubbly. Cook egg noodles according to package directions. Stir sour cream or low-fat yogurt and flour together; combine with stroganoff. Heat to a boil, stirring constantly. Reduce heat, simmer, and stir about 1 minute. Serve stroganoff over noodles. Makes 6 to 8 servings.

Summary of processes: Cut steak in bite-size pieces; chop 1 cup onion; mince 2 cloves garlic

Freeze in: 6-cup container

Serve with: Tomatoes stuffed with guacamole, corn on the cob

RECIPES

BALKAN MEATBALLS

1 egg
¼ cup milk
⅓ cup crushed seasoned croutons
¾ teaspoon salt
¾ teaspoon sugar
¼ teaspoon ground ginger
¼ teaspoon ground nutmeg
¼ teaspoon ground allspice
1 pound lean ground beef
½ pound ground turkey
1 tablespoon minced onion
1 8-ounce package wide egg noodles*
2 tablespoons margarine*
¼ cup all-purpose flour*
2 cups milk*
Parsley for garnish*

*I*n a medium mixing bowl, beat egg with milk. Mix in the crushed croutons, salt, sugar, and spices. Add beef, turkey, and onion; mix thoroughly. Preheat oven to broil and/or 550°. Shape meat mixture into meatballs the size of walnuts. Place meatballs on a rimmed cookie sheet; broil until lightly browned. Cool; put meatballs in a large bag and freeze them.

To prepare for serving, thaw meatballs. Cook noodles according to package directions. At the same time, make white sauce in a large skillet. Melt margarine over low heat. Add flour, stirring constantly until mixture is smooth and bubbly. Gradually stir in milk. Heat to boiling over medium heat, stirring constantly. Boil and stir 1 minute until thick and smooth. Add meatballs to sauce. Bring to a boil; reduce heat. Cover pan; simmer 15 minutes, stirring occasionally. Serve meatballs and sauce over wide egg noodles. Chop parsley; sprinkle over top. Makes 4 servings.

Summary of processes: Chop ⅔ cup onion

Freeze in: 1-gallon bag

Serve with: Cooked, fresh broccoli

MARINATED FLANK STEAK

½ cup vegetable oil
¼ cup soy sauce
¼ cup red wine vinegar
2 teaspoons Worcestershire sauce
½ teaspoon ground ginger
1 teaspoon minced garlic (1 clove)
1⅓ pounds flank steak

*M*ix first six ingredients for marinade. Put flank steak in a freezer bag, pour marinade over it, seal bag, and freeze.

To prepare for serving, thaw flank steak, remove from marinade, and barbecue 8 to 10 minutes per side; or set oven control to broil and/or 550°. Broil steak 6 inches from heat until brown, turning once, about 6 minutes on one side and 4 minutes on the other. Cut steak across grain at slanted angle into thin slices. Makes 4 servings.

Summary of processes: Mince 1 clove garlic

Freeze in: 1-gallon bag

Serve with: Twice-Baked Potatoes Deluxe (page 200), cooked zucchini

RECIPES

CHILI HAMBURGERS

1 pound lean ground beef or turkey
2 tablespoons finely chopped green bell pepper
1 tablespoon minced onion
1 tablespoon chili powder
1 tablespoon chili sauce
¼ teaspoon black pepper
½ teaspoon salt
4 hamburger buns*

*T*horoughly mix all ingredients except hamburger buns. Shape into 4 hamburger patties. Freeze in a large freezer bag, with waxed paper between each one.

To prepare for serving, thaw patties and hamburger buns. Grill or fry patties to desired pinkness in center. Serve on warmed hamburger buns. Makes 4 servings.

Summary of processes: Chop 2 tablespoons green bell pepper

Freeze in: 1-gallon bag

Serve with: French fries or baked beans, Jiffy Salad (page 196)

CHAPTER THREE
A Low-Fat Two-Week Entrée Plan

*H*e makes grass grow for
the cattle, and plants for man
to cultivate—bringing forth
food from the earth.

Psalm 104:14

Menu
· C A L E N D A R ·

Sunday	Monday	Tuesday	Wednesday	Thursday	Friday	Saturday
	Eat Out Cooking Day! *1*	Hearty Hamburger Tomato Stew *2*	Chinese Chicken Morsels *3*	Veggie Pizza *4*	Grilled Fish *5*	Chicken Spaghetti *6*
Mandarin Orange Chicken *7*	Vegetable Lasagna *8*	Stove-Top Barbecued Chicken *9*	Split Pea Soup *10*	Blackened Chicken Breast *11*	Chicken Cacciatore *12*	Pizza Roll-Ups *13*
Savory Beef *14*	Chili Verde *15*	*16*	*17*	*18*	*19*	*20*
21	*22*	*23*	*24*	*25*	*26*	*27*
28	*29*	*30*				

GROCERY SHOPPING AND STAPLES LISTS

An asterisk (*) after an item indicates that it should be stored until you cook the dish it will be served with. For example, the corn tortillas and salsa will not be used until the day you serve Chili Verde. Mark those items as a reminder that you will need them for an entrée.

When entrées require perishable foods to be refrigerated until served, you may want to prepare those dishes right away or buy the food the week you plan to make the dish. For example, fresh mushrooms would spoil by the end of a month.

For the low-fat entrée plan, you will need these food items as well as the ones in the staples list that follows.

GROCERY SHOPPING LIST

Canned Goods
1 16-ounce can corn
1 4-ounce can chopped green chilies
1 16-ounce can cut green beans
1 8-ounce bottle lemon juice (½ cup)
1 11-ounce can mandarin orange sections*
1 8-ounce can mushroom stems and pieces
1 2-ounce jar pimientos
1 11½-ounce jar salsa*
1 46-ounce can tomato juice
1 6-ounce can tomato paste
5 28-ounce cans Italian-style or plain crushed tomatoes in puree
1 3-ounce can sliced ripe olives

Grains, Noodles, Rice, and Seasonings
1 8-ounce package lasagna
1 8-ounce package dry pinto beans
1 16-ounce package regular rice (1 cup*)
6 sandwich rolls*
1 12-ounce package spaghetti
1 1½ package dry spaghetti sauce seasoning mix
1 8-ounce package wide egg noodles

1 16-ounce package spinach or wide egg noodles

1 12-ounce package dry, green split peas

1 dozen corn tortillas*

Frozen Foods

1¼ pounds frozen fish fillets (halibut, swordfish, or orange roughy)*

2 loaves frozen French, Italian, or all-purpose bread dough or Dawn's French Bread (page 183)

1 6-ounce can frozen orange juice concentrate

Dairy Products

8 ounces low-fat cheddar cheese

4 ounces low-fat Monterey Jack cheese

15 ounces part-skim mozzarella cheese

16 ounces low-fat ricotta cheese

Meat and Poultry

2 pounds skinned chicken pieces

7 pounds boneless, skinless chicken breasts

2 pounds lean ground beef or turkey

2 pounds beef round tip steak

½ pound cooked turkey ham

Produce

3 green bell peppers

1 small red bell pepper (opt.)

2 medium stems fresh broccoli

5 carrots (2¾ cups sliced)

1 bunch celery

4 cloves garlic

1¾ pounds fresh mushrooms (8 cups sliced)

1 bunch green onions

3 pounds brown or yellow onions (6 medium)

1 bunch fresh parsley
5 or 6 new potatoes
1 medium zucchini

STAPLES LIST

Make sure you have the following staples on hand; add those you don't have to the above shopping list:

dried basil leaves
bay leaf
beef bouillon cubes (2)
brown sugar
catsup (⅓ cup)
celery seed
chicken bouillon cubes (6)
chili powder
ground cloves
ground cumin
Dijon mustard (¼ cup)
dill weed
dry mustard
all-purpose flour
garlic powder
garlic salt
ground ginger
Italian herb seasoning
light mayonnaise
low-fat margarine
nonstick spray
olive oil
onion powder
dried oregano leaves
paprika
Parmesan cheese

pepper: cayenne, white, freshly ground black, and regular black

salt

soy sauce (¾ cup)

sugar

dried thyme leaves

vegetable oil (about ½ cup)

white vinegar

Worcestershire sauce (about 3 tablespoons)

FREEZER CONTAINERS

The following list of freezer containers or flat baking dishes will be needed for the entrées in the two-week cycle. They're not the only containers in which you could freeze these foods, but the list gives you an idea of the size and number of containers you'll need.

1 empty spice jar or small container:
Blackened Chicken

5 1-gallon freezer bags:
Pizza Roll-Ups (4), Chinese Chicken Morsels

8 1-quart freezer bags:
Pizza Roll-Ups (4), Grilled Fish, Blackened Chicken, Chicken Spaghetti, Chili Verde

Heavy aluminum foil:
Veggie Pizza, Vegetable Lasagna

1 12-inch pizza pan or 10-inch pie plate:
Veggie Pizza

2 4-cup freezer containers:
Stove-Top Barbecued Chicken, Mandarin Orange Chicken

1 5-cup freezer container:
Chili Verde

1 6-cup freezer container:
Split Pea Soup

2 8-cup freezer containers:
Savory Beef, Chicken Cacciatore

2 16-cup freezer containers:
Hearty Hamburger Tomato Stew, Chicken Spaghetti

1 13x9x2-inch baking dish:
Vegetable Lasagna

THE DAY BEFORE COOKING DAY

1. Freeze fish fillets, sandwich rolls, and 1½-pounds boneless, skinless chicken breasts for Blackened Chicken Breasts.

2. Use kitchen scissors or knife to cut 2 pounds raw, boneless chicken breasts into 1-inch cubes for Mandarin Orange Chicken and Chinese Chicken Morsels; refrigerate until needed.

3. In a large skillet, sauté remaining 3½-pounds boneless, skinless chicken breasts in a small amount of water until no longer pink in the center. Use kitchen scissors or knife to cut cooled chicken into 1-inch cubes. Store chicken in the refrigerator.

4. Set out appliances, bowls, canned goods, dry ingredients, freezer containers, and recipes.

5. Thaw 2 loaves of frozen bread dough in refrigerator overnight.

6. Rinse green split peas, and soak them covered with cold water overnight. Do the same for pinto beans.

COOKING DAY ASSEMBLY ORDER

Make sure you've cleared the table and counters of unnecessary kitchenware to allow plenty of working room. It also helps to have fresh, damp washcloths and towels for wiping your hands and the cooking area. The day will go smoother if you clean and organize as you work.

Before you prepare a recipe, gather all the spices and ingredients in the assembly area to save time and steps. When you finish the recipe, remove unneeded items, and wipe off the work space.

Slightly undercook regular rice and noodles (al dente) that will be frozen. When you reheat them, they will have a better consistency and won't turn mushy.

BEFORE ASSEMBLING DISHES

1. Put out 6-ounce can of frozen orange juice concentrate to thaw.

2. Brown 2 pounds of ground beef or turkey, drain, and blot on a paper towel.

3. Perform all chopping, grating, and slicing tasks.

> Turkey ham: cut into cubes.
> Beef: slice round tip steak into strips about 2 inches long.
> Onions: slice 2 onions; chop the rest.
> Green onions: chop onion bulbs only; discard green tops.
> Broccoli: chop fine tops of 2 medium stems including small amount of stems.
> Carrots: slice 2¾ cups.
> Celery: chop 1⅓ cups and slice 3 stalks, storing them in separate small bags.
> Garlic: mince 4 cloves.
> Mushrooms: slice all (8 cups).
> Parsley: chop the whole bunch, discarding most of stems.
> Green bell peppers: chop 2, slice 1.
> Red bell pepper: chop ½ cup.
> Zucchini: chop 1 cup.
> Mozzarella, cheddar, and Monterey Jack cheeses: grate all; put in separate bags.

4. Treat baking dishes and pie or pizza pans you will need with nonstick spray (check list of freezer containers on page 46).

5. As you assemble each group of the following entrées, allow them to cool if necessary, put them in storage containers and freeze.

ASSEMBLE GROUP 1 ENTRÉES

1. Combine ingredients for Italian Tomato Sauce and start it simmering.

2. Assemble and bake Veggie Pizza.

3. Roll out dough for Pizza Roll-Ups. Assemble and bake them.

4. Mix ingredients for Hearty Hamburger Tomato Stew and start it simmering.

5. As soon as the above dishes are completed and have cooled, label each one and freeze.

CHAPTER THREE

ASSEMBLE GROUP 2 ENTRÉES

1. Cook lasagna and broccoli for Vegetable Lasagna, and then finish assembling it.

2. Make marinade for Grilled Fish.

3. Label and freeze these dishes.

ASSEMBLE GROUP 3 ENTRÉES

1. Assemble and start cooking Split Pea Soup and Chili Verde.

2. Complete Savory Beef in a skillet. Allow to cool, label and freeze.

ASSEMBLE GROUP 4 ENTRÉES

1. Make Stove-Top Barbecued Chicken in one large skillet or pan with lid and Chicken Cacciatore in another.

2. While these are simmering, assemble Chinese Chicken Morsels.

3. Mix spices for Blackened Chicken Breasts.

4. Prepare Mandarin Orange Chicken.

5. Assemble Chicken Spaghetti, cooking noodles while chicken and tomato sauce are simmering.

6. Complete Split Pea Soup and Chili Verde; allow to cool.

7. Label and freeze this last batch of dishes.

Take a minute to enjoy looking into your freezer at all the food you've prepared!

RECIPES FOR THE LOW-FAT ENTRÉE PLAN

Each recipe offers complete instructions on how to prepare the dish. Food items with an asterisk (*) won't be prepared until you serve the entrée. For recipes calling for oven baking, preheat oven for about 10 minutes.

"Summary of processes" gives a quick overview of foods that need to be chopped, diced, grated, or sliced. "Freeze in" tells what bags and containers will be needed to freeze each entrée. "Serve with" offers suggestions of foods to accompany the meal. Some of the recipes for those foods are included in chapter 8; page numbers are indicated for easy reference. "Note" includes special instructions on how the entrée can be used in other ways.

ITALIAN TOMATO SAUCE

3 28-ounce cans Italian-style or plain crushed tomatoes in puree
3 tablespoons sugar
3 tablespoons Italian herb seasoning
6 tablespoons chopped, fresh parsley
3 tablespoons dried basil leaves
3 teaspoons garlic salt
1½ teaspoons pepper

*M*ix all the ingredients in a heavy, large pot. Bring to a boil; reduce heat. Simmer 15 minutes, stirring occasionally. Save 3½ cups sauce for Vegetable Lasagna and 2 cups for Veggie Pizza. Divide remaining sauce into four 1-cup portions, and put in four 1-quart bags for Pizza Roll-Ups. Makes 9½ cups.

Summary of Processes: Chop 6 tablespoons parsley

Freeze in: 4 1-quart bags

RECIPES

VEGGIE PIZZA

¼ cup chopped onion
¼ cup chopped red bell pepper (opt.)
¼ cup chopped green bell pepper
1 cup chopped zucchini
1 cup sliced fresh mushrooms
1 tablespoon vegetable oil
½ cup grated part-skim mozzarella cheese
1 loaf frozen French, Italian or all-purpose bread dough, or Dawn's
    French Bread (page 183)
2 cups Italian Tomato Sauce

*P*reheat oven to 400°. Sauté vegetables in oil, drain well, and allow to cool. Stir in cheese. Roll dough into a ½-inch-thick circle. Put dough on a 12-inch pizza pan or 10-inch pie plate. Spread Italian Tomato Sauce on pizza. Spoon vegetable mixture over sauce. Bake pizza for 20 minutes. Cool, cover pizza with heavy aluminum foil, and freeze.

To prepare for serving, thaw and then heat pizza in a preheated 400° oven for about 20 minutes. Makes 6 servings.

Summary of processes: Chop ¼ cup onion, ¼ cup red bell pepper, ¼ cup green bell pepper, 1 cup zucchini; slice 1 cup fresh mushrooms; grate ½ cup part-skim mozzarella cheese

Freeze in: 12-inch pizza pan or 10-inch pie pan; heavy aluminum foil

Serve with: Lemon gelatin with pears

Note: A tasty addition to this pizza is ½ pound browned turkey sausage, 1 teaspoon parsley, 1 teaspoon dried basil leaves, 1 teaspoon dried oregano leaves, and ½ teaspoon salt.

CHAPTER THREE

PIZZA ROLL-UPS

1 loaf frozen French, Italian, or all-purpose bread dough, or Dawn's
    French Bread (page 183)
1 pound lean ground beef or turkey (2½ cups browned)
1 teaspoon salt
½ teaspoon pepper
2 cups grated part-skim mozzarella cheese
1 teaspoon Italian herb seasoning
1 tablespoon chopped fresh parsley
4 cups Italian Tomato Sauce*

*T*haw dough; roll it into a 14x24-inch rectangle about ¼-inch thick. Brown ground beef or turkey; stir in remaining ingredients except Italian Tomato Sauce. Spoon filling evenly onto dough, slightly pressing filling into dough.

Roll dough lengthwise like a jelly roll, and cut into 24 1-inch slices. Treat 2 rimmed cookie sheets with nonstick spray; lay slices on sheets about an inch apart. Preheat oven to 400°. Let roll-ups sit for 10 minutes. Bake for 20 to 25 minutes or till golden brown. Cool roll-ups, and freeze in 4 1-gallon bags, 6 per bag. Slip a 1-quart bag with 1 cup sauce into each bag of Pizza Roll-Ups.

To prepare, thaw roll-ups and warm them in a preheated 400° oven for 10 minutes. Or put them frozen in the microwave; heat on high for about 2 minutes. Serve with warmed Italian Tomato Sauce. Makes 24 servings.

Summary of processes: Chop 1 tablespoon parsley; grate 2 cups part-skim mozzarella cheese

Freeze in: 4 1-gallon bags, Roll-Ups; 4 1-quart bags, Italian Tomato Sauce

Serve with: Tossed green salad

Note: These roll-ups are super for picnics or nights when the family must eat in shifts. They can be eaten warm or cold. They're also a favorite with kids and an easy snack.

RECIPES

HEARTY HAMBURGER TOMATO STEW

1 pound lean ground beef or turkey (2½ cups browned)
1¼ cups chopped onion
2 cups peeled and sliced carrots
1 cup chopped green bell pepper
1 cup sliced fresh mushrooms
1 16-ounce can cut green beans, drained
1 16-ounce can corn, drained
3 stalks sliced celery
1 46-ounce can tomato juice
2 teaspoons sugar
1 teaspoon celery seed
Salt and pepper to taste

*B*rown ground beef or turkey in a large saucepan. Mix in remaining ingredients; bring to a boil; reduce heat. Simmer, covered, 30 minutes, stirring occasionally. Cool and freeze.

To prepare for serving, thaw stew. Then bring to a boil; reduce heat; simmer 10 minutes. Makes 8 servings.

Summary of processes: Chop 1¼ cups onion and 1 cup green bell pepper; peel and slice 2 cups carrots, 1 cup fresh mushrooms, and 3 stalks celery

Freeze in: 16-cup container

Serve with: Cornbread or wheat crackers

VEGETABLE LASAGNA

1 8-ounce package lasagna
2 medium stems finely chopped broccoli florets
1 16-ounce carton low-fat ricotta cheese
1 cup grated part-skim mozzarella cheese
1 8-ounce can mushroom stems and pieces, drained
2 chopped green onion bulbs (without greens)
2 teaspoons dried basil leaves
1½ teaspoons crumbled dried oregano leaves
¼ cup finely chopped fresh parsley
Dash of fresh ground black pepper
3½ cups Italian Tomato Sauce

*B*oil lasagna 10 minutes or until al dente, stirring occasionally to prevent noodles from sticking. Drain noodles, rinse in cold water, and then lay them next to each other on waxed paper to dry. Cook broccoli 5 minutes in boiling water.

Combine cheeses, vegetables, herbs, and pepper in a medium bowl. In a 13x9x2-inch dish that has been treated with nonstick spray, layer lasagna noodles and spread with half the cheese mixture and half the tomato sauce. Repeat process, topping with noodles and covering with sauce. Wrap dish with foil and freeze.

To prepare for serving, thaw dish. Preheat oven to 350°. Cover and bake for 20 minutes. Remove foil, and bake 15 to 20 minutes more until heated through. Makes 12 servings.

Summary of processes: Grate 1 cup part-skim mozzarella cheese; chop 2 medium broccoli stems, 2 green onion bulbs, ¼ cup parsley

Freeze in: 13x9x2-inch baking dish

Serve with: Fresh fruit salad, bread sticks

Note: For an alternate way to prepare this entrée, use large shell pasta. Cook pasta as directed on package until al dente. Stuff each shell with cheese mixture. Freeze stuffed shells on a rimmed baking sheet. When they're hard, transfer them to a freezer bag. Freeze sauce in a separate bag taped to pasta bag. Thaw number of shells and amount of sauce desired. Warm them in a preheated 350° oven about 20 minutes. Serve shells with warmed sauce poured over them.

GRILLED FISH

1¼ pounds frozen fish fillets (halibut, swordfish, or orange roughy)*
5 or 6 new potatoes*
½ cup soy sauce
¼ cup water
¼ chicken bouillon cube
2 tablespoons olive oil
1 tablespoon brown sugar
2 teaspoons minced garlic (2 cloves)
½ teaspoon ground ginger

*F*reeze fish fillets, and store new potatoes until you're ready to serve them. Whisk remaining ingredients in a small bowl to make marinade. Freeze in a plastic bag taped to fish fillet package.

To prepare for serving, thaw marinade and fish fillets. Marinate fish in refrigerator 30 minutes. Prepare new potatoes. Heat 1 cup salted water to a boil; add potatoes. Cover, heat till boiling; then reduce heat. Simmer, tightly covered, until tender, 30 to 35 minutes; drain.

At the same time, remove fish from marinade. Preheat oven to broil and/or 550°. Broil or grill fish for 10 minutes per inch of thickness or until fish flakes easily with a fork. Baste frequently with marinade while cooking. If fish is more than 1-inch thick, turn once during cooking. Makes 4 servings.

Summary of processes: Mince 2 garlic cloves

Freeze in: 1-quart bag taped to fish fillet package

Serve with: Tossed green salad

SPLIT PEA SOUP

1 12-ounce package dry, green split peas
3 cups water
½ pound cooked, cubed turkey ham
¾ teaspoon onion powder
⅛ teaspoon dried thyme leaves
⅛ teaspoon freshly ground pepper
⅓ cup chopped celery
¾ cup peeled and sliced carrots
1 cup chopped onion
1 bay leaf
Salt to taste

*R*inse split peas, soak them in cold water overnight; drain. Put peas with remaining ingredients in a large saucepan. Bring to a boil; reduce heat. Stirring occasionally, simmer about 2 hours until peas are tender and turn pasty. Cool and freeze.

To serve, thaw peas and simmer until warmed through. If peas are too condensed, add water to make consistency of thick soup. Makes 6 servings.

Summary of processes: Soak split peas in water overnight; cut ham into cubes; peel and slice ¾ cup carrots; chop 1 cup onion, ⅓ cup celery

Freeze in: 6-cup container

Serve with: Orange slices or canned peaches, cornbread

RECIPES

CHILI VERDE

1 8-ounce package dry pinto beans (1¼ cups)
1 pound boneless, skinless chicken breasts
1 4-ounce can chopped green chilies
1 teaspoon ground cumin
¾ teaspoon dried oregano leaves
⅛ teaspoon ground cloves
⅛ teaspoon cayenne pepper
3 cups water
3 chicken bouillon cubes
1 teaspoon minced garlic (1 clove)
1 teaspoon salt
⅔ cup finely chopped onion
1 cup grated low-fat Monterey Jack cheese*
1 11½-ounce jar salsa*
1 dozen corn tortillas*

*R*inse pinto beans, soak them in cold water overnight, then drain. Cut chicken into 1-inch cubes; cook until no longer pink in small amount of water or vegetable oil. Combine chicken with chilies and seasonings; refrigerate until needed. At the same time, combine beans, water, bouillon cubes, garlic, salt, and onion in a large pot; bring to a boil.

Reduce heat and simmer until beans are soft, about 1 hour. Add more water if necessary.

Combine chicken and spices with beans; simmer 10 minutes more. Cool and freeze. Grate cheese, put it in a 1-quart bag, and attach it to the freezer container with the chili.

To serve, thaw chili and cheese. Simmer chili 30 minutes, stirring occasionally. Top chili with salsa and grated cheese; serve on warmed corn tortillas. Makes 5 servings.

Summary of processes: Soak ½ pound pinto beans overnight; cut 1 pound boneless chicken into cubes; finely chop ⅔ cup onion; grate 1 cup low-fat Monterey Jack cheese

Freeze in: 5-cup container; 1-quart bag

Serve with: Tossed green salad

SAVORY BEEF

2 pounds beef round tip steak
Freshly ground black pepper to taste
1 cup sliced fresh mushrooms
1 sliced onion
3 tablespoons vegetable oil
3 tablespoons all-purpose flour
2 cups water
2 beef bouillon cubes
2 tablespoons tomato paste
1 teaspoon dry mustard
¼ teaspoon dried oregano leaves
¼ teaspoon dill weed
2 tablespoons Worcestershire sauce
1 8-ounce package wide egg noodles*

*C*ut beef into thin strips about 2 inches long. Sprinkle beef with pepper, and set meat aside in a cool place. In a heavy skillet, sauté mushrooms and onion in oil until golden; remove them from skillet. Put meat in same skillet; cook and stir steak quickly on all sides until it's brown but still rare in the center. Remove meat, and set aside.

Blend flour into the drippings in skillet, gradually adding water and beef bouillon. Bring to a boil. Stir constantly until smooth and slightly thick. Mix in tomato paste, dry mustard, oregano, dill weed, and Worcestershire sauce. Stir meat, mushrooms, and onion into sauce. Cool meat mixture and freeze.

To prepare for serving, thaw beef. Prepare noodles according to package directions. Heat beef in a saucepan over medium heat, stirring constantly until bubbly. Serve meat over noodles. Makes 6 servings.

Summary of processes: Slice 1 cup fresh mushrooms and 1 onion

Freeze in: 8-cup container

Serve with: French-cut green beans

Note: Use any leftover beef for sandwiches.

RECIPES

STOVE-TOP BARBECUED CHICKEN

1 teaspoon vegetable oil
1 cup finely chopped onion
⅓ cup catsup
⅓ cup water
4 teaspoons white vinegar
4 teaspoons brown sugar
1½ teaspoons Worcestershire sauce
½ teaspoon chili powder
¼ teaspoon crushed celery seed
2 pounds skinned chicken pieces
1 16-ounce package spinach or wide egg noodles (use half)*

*H*eat oil in a large, nonstick skillet; sauté onion until tender. Stir in catsup, water, vinegar, brown sugar, Worcestershire sauce, chili powder, and celery seed. Bring sauce to a boil. Add the chicken to the skillet, placing the side down that has the skin removed; spoon sauce over the pieces. Bring to a boil; reduce heat. Cover and simmer 30 minutes. Turn chicken pieces, and simmer, covered, for about 20 minutes more or until chicken is cooked through. Cool and freeze chicken and sauce.

To prepare for serving, thaw chicken and sauce; put in a large skillet and cook over medium heat, stirring constantly until bubbly. Cook half package of spinach or egg noodles according to directions; serve chicken over noodles. Makes 4 servings.

Summary of processes: Chop 1 cup onion

Freeze in: 4-cup container

Serve with: Corn on the cob, Low-Calorie Chocolate Cake (page 194)

CHAPTER THREE

CHICKEN CACCIATORE

1 pound boneless, skinless chicken breasts (2 cups cooked)
1 tablespoon vegetable oil
1 sliced medium onion
½ sliced green bell pepper
2 cups sliced fresh mushrooms
1 teaspoon minced garlic (1 clove)
1 28-ounce can Italian-style or plain crushed tomatoes in puree
2 tablespoons chopped fresh parsley
1 teaspoon salt
¼ teaspoon pepper
2 teaspoons Italian herb seasoning
1 teaspoon dried basil leaves
Parmesan cheese*
1 16-ounce package spinach or wide egg noodles (use half)*

*C*ut chicken into 1-inch cubes. In a large skillet, sauté chicken in vegetable oil until no longer pink in the center. Remove chicken from skillet and sauté onion, green bell pepper, mushrooms, and garlic until onion is transparent. Add chicken and remaining ingredients except Parmesan cheese and noodles to the skillet. Simmer 15 minutes. Allow sauce to cool, put in an 8-cup container or dish, and freeze.

To serve, thaw dish and preheat oven to 350°. Bake chicken in a 13x9x2-inch baking dish for 35 minutes. Cook half package spinach or egg noodles according to directions. Serve chicken over noodles, and sprinkle on Parmesan cheese. Makes 6 servings.

Summary of processes: Cut 1 pound chicken into cubes; slice 1 medium onion, ½ green bell pepper, 2 cups fresh mushrooms; mince 1 clove garlic

Freeze in: 8-cup container or dish

Serve with: Cooked baby carrots, Dawn's French Bread (page 183)

CHINESE CHICKEN MORSELS

1 pound boneless, skinless chicken breasts (2 cups)
½ cup lemon juice
¼ cup soy sauce
¼ cup Dijon mustard
2 teaspoons vegetable oil
¼ teaspoon cayenne pepper
1 cup regular, uncooked rice*

*C*ut chicken breasts (kitchen scissors work best) into 1-inch cubes. Mix lemon juice, soy sauce, mustard, oil, and pepper. Put marinade and chicken cubes in a 1-gallon bag and store in the freezer.

To prepare for serving, thaw chicken and remove from marinade. Warm marinade in a small saucepan. Place cubes about an inch apart on broiler pan treated with nonstick spray. Broil 4 to 5 inches from heat for 7 minutes, brushing with marinade once. Turn chicken cubes and broil another 4 minutes. Meanwhile, prepare rice according to package directions. Heat remaining marinade and serve over rice. Makes 4 to 5 servings.

Summary of processes: Cut chicken into 1-inch cubes

Freeze in: 1-gallon bag

Serve with: Sliced, fresh tomatoes or tossed salad, Spicy Pumpkin Muffins (page 188)

Note: For a luncheon alternative, toss sautéed or broiled chicken morsels with mixed salad greens, shredded carrots, cherry tomatoes, chopped green bell pepper, sliced water chestnuts, and croutons. Use your favorite low-calorie dressing.

BLACKENED CHICKEN BREASTS

1½ pounds boneless, skinless chicken breasts*
6 sandwich rolls*
Spice Mix*
    2 teaspoons paprika
    1 teaspoon onion powder
    1 teaspoon garlic powder
    ¼ teaspoon cayenne pepper
    ½ teaspoon white pepper
    ½ teaspoon black pepper
    ½ teaspoon salt
    ½ teaspoon dried thyme leaves
    ½ teaspoon dried oregano leaves
¼ cup (½ stick) melted low-fat margarine or light mayonnaise*
2 tablespoons vegetable oil*
Low-fat margarine or light mayonnaise*

*F*reeze chicken and sandwich rolls until ready to serve. Mix spices; store in a covered container such as an empty spice jar, which you've labeled "Blackened Chicken Spices."

To serve, thaw rolls and chicken. Coat each piece of chicken with about 1 tablespoon spice mix. The mixture is hot and spicy, so adjust amount for taste of each person. Using a pastry brush, baste each piece of chicken with melted, low-fat margarine or light mayonnaise. Grill chicken, basting with low-fat margarine or mayonnaise after turning once. Grill about 10 minutes or until no longer pink in the middle. Or cook chicken in a large, nonstick skillet in hot oil over medium heat. Cook, turning chicken once, until it's done, about 10 minutes. Serve on sandwich rolls spread with a little margarine or light mayonnaise. Makes 6 servings.

Summary of processes: Mix spices

Freeze in: 1-quart bag

Serve with: Applesauce, carrot and celery strips

Note: Use spice mix on your favorite fish fillets.

MANDARIN ORANGE CHICKEN

1 pound boneless, skinless chicken breasts (2 cups)
1 tablespoon vegetable oil
2 cups sliced, fresh mushrooms
2 teaspoons all-purpose flour
⅔ cup water
1 6-ounce can frozen orange juice concentrate, thawed
½ cup thinly sliced green onion bulbs (without greens)
2 chicken bouillon cubes
1 cup regular, uncooked rice*
1 11-ounce can mandarin orange sections, drained*

*C*ut chicken into 1-inch chunks with kitchen scissors or knife. Heat oil in large skillet; add chicken, and cook on medium high until browned on both sides. Remove and set chicken aside. In the same skillet, cook mushrooms over medium high, stirring constantly. Sprinkle flour over mushrooms, stirring quickly to combine. Gradually stir in water, orange juice concentrate, green onions, and bouillon cubes. Stirring constantly, bring to a boil. Reduce heat, add chicken, and let simmer 3 to 4 minutes. Cool and freeze.

To serve, thaw chicken mixture, and cook rice according to package directions. Heat chicken mixture in a saucepan until bubbly, stir in drained orange segments, and heat through. Combine with cooked rice and serve. Makes 4 servings.

Summary of processes: Cut 1 pound chicken into chunks; slice 2 cups fresh mushrooms, ½ cup green onion bulbs

Freeze in: 4-cup container

Serve with: French-cut green beans, biscuits

CHICKEN SPAGHETTI

1 12-ounce package spaghetti (semolina)
1½ pounds boneless, skinless chicken breasts (3 cups cooked)
1 28-ounce can Italian-style or plain crushed tomatoes in puree
1 2-ounce jar pimientos
1 cup chopped green bell pepper
1 cup chopped celery
1 cup sliced fresh mushrooms
1½ cups chopped onion
1 3-ounce can sliced ripe olives
1 package dry spaghetti sauce seasoning
Salt and pepper to taste
2 cups grated low-fat cheddar cheese*

*C*ook spaghetti until al dente; drain. At the same time, cut chicken into 1-inch cubes; cook chicken in a small amount of water until no longer pink in the center. In a large pot, combine chicken with remaining ingredients except cheese. Bring mixture to a boil; reduce heat. Simmer for 15 minutes, stirring occasionally. Add cooked spaghetti to sauce. Cool and freeze in 16-cup container; tape 1-quart bag with cheese to container.

To prepare for serving, thaw cheese and spaghetti. Preheat oven to 325°; pour spaghetti into an oven-proof casserole dish and bake for 40 minutes. Top spaghetti with cheese; return spaghetti to oven for 5 minutes more or until cheese melts. Makes 10 servings.

Summary of processes: Cut 1½ pounds chicken into 1-inch cubes; chop 1 cup green bell pepper, 1 cup celery, and 1½ cups onion; slice 1 cup fresh mushrooms; grate 2 cups low-fat cheddar cheese

Freeze in: 16-cup container; 1-quart bag

Serve with: Tossed green salad, Cheesy-Herb Bread (page 180)

CHAPTER FOUR

Two-Week Entrée Plan B

She watches over the affairs
of her household and does not
eat the bread of idleness.

Proverbs 31:27

Menu
· C A L E N D A R ·

Sunday	Monday	Tuesday	Wednesday	Thursday	Friday	Saturday
	Eat Out Cooking Day! 1	Herbed Chicken 2	Biscuit Beef Bake 3	French Stuffed Potatoes 4	Chicken Nuggets 5	Playoff Burgers 6
Farmer's Casserole 7	Poppy Turkey 8	Crab Shells 9	Country Captain 10	Denise's Black Beans 11	Spicy Garlic Chicken Pizza 12	London Broil 13
Mexican Chicken Lasagna 14	Sopa de Maiz 15	16	17	18	19	20
21	22	23	24	25	26	27
28	29	30				

GROCERY SHOPPING AND STAPLES LISTS

An asterisk(*) after an item indicates it can be stored until you cook that dish. For example, the can of mandarin oranges will not be needed until the day you serve Country Captain. Mark those items before you put them away as a reminder that you will need them for an entrée.

When entrées require perishable foods to be refrigerated until served, you may want to use those dishes right away or buy the food the week you plan to prepare the dish.

For two-week entrée Plan B you will need these food items as well as the ones on the staples list that follows.

GROCERY SHOPPING LIST

Canned Goods

 1 4-ounce can mushroom stems and pieces

 1 10¾-ounce can cream of mushroom soup

 5 14½-ounce cans stewed tomatoes

 1 14½-ounce can Mexican-style stewed tomatoes

 2 8-ounce cans tomato sauce

 1 15-ounce can tomato sauce

 ½ cup salsa, medium or mild

 5 15-ounce cans black beans

 2 4-ounce cans chopped green chilis

 1 12-ounce can evaporated milk or evaporated skim milk

Grains, Pasta, and Rice

 2 5.7-ounce boxes of couscous* (or enough to serve 6)

 1 16-ounce (12-inch) Italian bread shell (Boboli brand)

 32-ounce bag of rice*

 2 10-ounce boxes uncooked lasagna noodles

 8 ounces linguini

 6 whole wheat buns or Kaiser rolls

 12 jumbo pasta shells

Dry Ingredients and Seasonings

 ½ cup dried bread crumbs—Italian style

 ¼ cup slivered almonds

1 1¼-ounce package taco seasoning
1 10½-ounce bag of Fritos or corn chips*

Frozen Foods

2 16-ounce bags frozen corn
26-ounce bag frozen shredded hash brown potatoes

Dairy Products

2 sticks butter or margarine
1¼ cups grated Parmesan cheese
3 cups (12 ounces) grated Monterey Jack cheese
1 cup (4 ounces) Monterey Jack cheese with jalapeño peppers (also called hot pepper cheese)
2 ounces mozzarella cheese, grated
7 eggs
1 16-ounce container ricotta cheese
4½ cups milk
½ cup each grated Swiss and cheddar cheese
1 cup cottage cheese
1 8-ounce package light cream cheese
1 cup plain low-fat yogurt
1 12-ounce package Hungry Jack buttermilk biscuits*
1 cup of sour cream

Meat, Poultry, and Seafood

6 pounds boneless, skinless chicken breasts
5 to 6 pounds chicken pieces
2 pounds ground turkey
4 pounds lean ground beef
2 pounds London broil
⅓ pound fully cooked ham
1 pound smoked sausage links (i.e., Lit'l Smokies)
½ pound crabmeat or imitation crabmeat

Produce

5 to 6 large bunches green onions

11 cloves garlic

½ cup fresh parsley

¼ cup currants or raisins

4 medium yellow onions

1 tomato*

1 avocado*

4 large baking potatoes*

2 green bell peppers

1 bunch celery

1 lemon

STAPLES LIST

A-1 sauce

all-purpose flour

basil

bay leaves

black pepper

brown sugar

cayenne pepper

chili powder

cornstarch

cumin

curry powder

Dijon mustard

dried oregano leaves

dried thyme leaves

ground ginger

ground mace or nutmeg

chicken bouillon cubes (4)

onion salt

poppy seeds

salsa

salt

soy sauce

sugar

vegetable oil

white vinegar

Worcestershire sauce

FREEZER CONTAINERS

The following list of freezer containers or flat baking dishes will be needed for the entrées in two-week entrée plan B. They're not the only containers in which you could freeze these foods, but the list gives you an idea of the size and number of containers you'll need.

9 1-gallon freezer bags:
Chicken Nuggets, Spicy Garlic Chicken Pizza, Herbed Chicken, Country Captain, French Stuffed Potatoes, Poppy Turkey (2), Playoff Burgers, London Broil

5 1-quart freezer bags:
Chicken Nuggets, Spicy Garlic Chicken Pizza (2), French Stuffed Potatoes, Playoff Burgers

2 13x9x2-inch baking dishes:
Mexican Chicken Lasagna, Farmer's Casserole

1 10-inch round baking dish:
Crab Shells

1 5-cup container:
Biscuit Beef Bake

1 6-cup container:
Sopa de Maiz

1 10-cup container:
Denise's Black Beans

THE DAY BEFORE COOKING DAY

1. Store the Hungry Jack buttermilk biscuits, rice, couscous, Fritos, 1 tomato, 1 avocado, 4 large baking potatoes, and linguini in the refrigerator or cupboard until the day you will be serving the corresponding entrée. Be sure to label each so you won't forget and use them for other dishes.

2. Bring 3 pounds boneless, skinless chicken breasts to boil in a large pot in at least 6 cups of water. Boil gently until chicken is tender and no longer pink in the center—about 15 minutes. Drain, reserving 3 cups chicken broth. Chop the cooked chicken. Refrigerate until ready to use on cooking day.

3. Set out appliances, canned goods, dry ingredients, freezer containers, and recipes.

COOKING DAY ASSEMBLY ORDER

Make sure you've cleared the table and counters of unnecessary kitchenware to allow plenty of working room. It also helps to have fresh, damp washcloths and towels for wiping your hands and the cooking area. The day will go a lot smoother if you clean and organize as you work.

Before you prepare a recipe, gather all the spices and ingredients in the assembly area to save time and steps. When you finish the recipe, remove unneeded items and wipe off the work space.

BEFORE ASSEMBLING DISHES

1. Perform all chopping, crushing, grating, and slicing tasks.
> Parsley: chop ¼ cup.
> Celery: chop 1½ cups.
> Green pepper: chop 2 cups.
> Green onions: slice 5 to 6 large bunches to make 2½ cups.
> Monterey Jack cheese with jalepeño peppers: grate 1 cup.
> Mozzarella cheese: grate ½ cup.
> Swiss cheese: grate ½ cup.
> Lemon zest: grate 2 tablespoons.
> Boneless chicken breasts: cube 3 pounds (use kitchen scissors for best results).
> Ham: cube 1 cup.

Smoked sausage: slice 1 pound.
Onions: chop 3¾ cups.
Garlic: mince 10 cloves.

2. Assemble Denise's Black Beans in a slow cooker.

ASSEMBLE CHICKEN DISHES

1. Assemble Chicken Nuggets.

2. Assemble Spicy Garlic Chicken.

3. While chicken is marinating in refrigerator, assemble Herbed Chicken.

4. Assemble Country Captain.

5. Complete Spicy Garlic Chicken Pizza and freeze.

6. Assemble Mexican Chicken Lasagna.

7. Assemble Sopa de Maiz.

8. Label and freeze chicken dishes.

ASSEMBLE BEEF AND GROUND TURKEY DISHES

1. In 2 skillets, brown ground beef and onions for Biscuit Beef Bake, and ground beef for French Stuffed Potatoes. Finish one at a time.

2. Assemble Poppy Turkey.

3. Assemble Playoff Burgers.

4. Make sauce for London Broil.

5. Label and freeze beef and ground turkey dishes.

ASSEMBLE SEAFOOD AND MISCELLANEOUS DISHES

1. Assemble Crab Shells.

2. Assemble Farmer's Casserole.

3. Label and freeze these two dishes.

4. Cool Denise's Black Beans after they've cooked 8 hours. Label and freeze.

RECIPES FOR TWO-WEEK ENTRÉE PLAN B

Each recipe offers complete instructions on how to prepare the dish. Food items with an asterisk (*) won't be prepared until you serve the entrée. For recipes calling for oven baking, preheat oven for about 10 minutes.

"Summary of processes" gives a quick overview of foods that need to be chopped, diced, grated, or sliced. "Freeze in" tells what bags and containers will be needed to freeze each entrée. "Serve with" offers suggestions of foods to accompany the meal. Some of the recipes for those foods are included in chapter 8; page numbers are indicated for easy reference. "Note" includes special instructions on how the entrée can be used in other ways.

DENISE'S BLACK BEANS

1 pound smoked sausage cut into pieces (i.e., Lit'l Smokies)
3 15-ounce cans black beans, drained
1½ cups chopped onion
1½ cups chopped green bell pepper
1½ cups chopped celery
4 teaspoons minced garlic (4 cloves)
2 teaspoons dried thyme leaves
1½ teaspoons dried oregano leaves
1½ teaspoons pepper
¼ teaspoon cayenne pepper
1 chicken bouillon cube
5 bay leaves
1 8-ounce can tomato sauce
1 cup water
Rice* (to serve 8)

*C*ombine all ingredients, except rice, in a slow cooker. Cook on low for 8 hours. Remove bay leaves. Cool to room temperature and freeze.

When preparing to serve, heat to boiling and simmer 15 minutes. Serve over hot, cooked rice. Makes 8 servings.

Summary of processes: Chop 1½ cups onion, 1½ cups green pepper, and 1½ cups celery; mince 4 cloves garlic

Serve with: Rice, Blueberry Peach Fruit Crisp (page 193)

Freeze in: 1 6-cup container

CHICKEN NUGGETS

2 pounds boneless, skinless chicken breasts
3 tablespoons margarine or butter, melted
2 teaspoons Worcestershire sauce
½ cup dried bread crumbs—Italian style
⅓ cup grated Parmesan cheese

*C*ut chicken into 1-inch pieces (kitchen shears work best). Combine chicken, melted margarine, and Worcestershire in a 1-quart freezer bag. Combine the bread crumbs and Parmesan cheese in a second freezer bag. Tape the two bags together. Label and freeze.

To prepare for serving, thaw and remove the chicken pieces from marinade. Shake them in the bread crumb bag to coat, a few at a time. Preheat oven to 450°. Arrange chicken on a greased cookie sheet. Bake for 7 to 9 minutes or until no longer pink in the center. Makes 4 servings.

Summary of processes: Cut 2 pounds boneless, skinless chicken into 1-inch pieces

Freeze in: 1-gallon bag; 1-quart bag

Serve with: Chips and dips; green bean casserole; catsup or barbecue sauce for dipping

RECIPES

SPICY GARLIC CHICKEN PIZZA

12 ounces boneless, skinless chicken breasts
½ cup sliced green onion, divided
2 cloves garlic, minced
2 tablespoons white vinegar
2 tablespoons soy sauce
3 tablespoons vegetable oil, divided
¼ teaspoon cayenne pepper
¼ teaspoon black pepper
1 tablespoon water
1 tablespoon cornstarch
1 16-ounce (12-inch) Italian bread shell (Boboli brand)
½ cup grated Monterey Jack cheese
½ cup grated mozzarella cheese
¼ cup slivered almonds

*C*ut chicken into 1-inch pieces (kitchen shears work best). In a large bowl combine green onion, minced garlic, vinegar, soy sauce, 2 tablespoons oil, and the cayenne and black pepper. Add the chicken pieces; stir to coat. Refrigerate the chicken in the soy sauce for 30 minutes. Drain, reserving marinade.

Heat remaining oil in a large skillet on medium high; add chicken pieces. Cook and stir about 5 to 7 minutes or until no longer pink. Add 1 tablespoon water and stir cornstarch into reserved marinade. Add to skillet. Cook and stir until thickened and bubbly. Cool and freeze. While chicken is cooking, combine the grated cheeses in a 1-quart bag, the remaining green onions in a 1-quart bag and the nuts in another 1-quart bag. Tape all three bags together to the package of the Italian bread shell.

To prepare for serving, thaw chicken mixture. Preheat oven to 400°. Spoon mixture evenly atop bread shell. Sprinkle with cheese. Bake, uncovered, for 12 minutes. Top with slivered almonds. Return to oven for 2 minutes more. Makes 4 servings.

Summary of processes: Cut 12 ounces boneless, skinless chicken into 1-inch pieces; slice ½ cup green onion; mince 2 cloves garlic; grate ½ cup Monterey Jack cheese and ½ cup mozzarella cheese

Freeze in: 1-gallon bag; 2 1-quart bags

Serve with: Spinach salad with creamy mustard dressing

HERBED CHICKEN

2½ to 3 pounds chicken pieces
1 10¾-ounce can cream of mushroom soup
1 teaspoon grated lemon zest
1½ tablespoons lemon juice
½ teaspoon salt
1 teaspoon dried basil leaves
1 teaspoon dried oregano leaves
Rice* (to serve 6)

*P*lace chicken in a 1-gallon freezer bag. In a small bowl, combine the remaining ingredients, except rice. Pour over the chicken and freeze.

To prepare for serving, thaw chicken mixture. Preheat oven to 350°. Place mixture in a 13x9x2-inch baking dish, treated with nonstick spray. Cover and bake for 1¼ hours. Serve over hot, cooked rice. Makes 6 servings.

Summary of processes: Grate 1 tablespoon lemon zest

Freeze in: 1-gallon bag

Serve with: French-cut green beans

COUNTRY CAPTAIN

1 14½-ounce can stewed tomatoes (undrained)
¼ cup fresh parsley, chopped
¼ cup currants or raisins
1 tablespoon curry powder
½ chicken bouillon cube
½ teaspoon ground mace or nutmeg
¼ teaspoon sugar
1 teaspoon salt
2½ to 3 pounds chicken pieces
1 tablespoon cornstarch
1 tablespoon cold water
Hot cooked couscous* (to serve 6)

*I*n a medium bowl, stir together tomatoes, parsley, currants or raisins, curry powder, bouillon cube, mace or nutmeg, sugar, and salt. Pour over chicken in freezer bag. Label and freeze.

To prepare for serving, place thawed chicken and sauce in large skillet. Bring mixture to boiling; reduce heat. Cover and simmer for 20 minutes or until chicken is no longer pink. Remove chicken from skillet; keep warm. Skim fat from mixture in skillet. In a small bowl stir together cornstarch and cold water; add to skillet. Cook and stir till thickened and bubbly. Cook and stir 2 minutes more. Serve over couscous or hot rice. Sprinkle with almonds, if desired. Makes 6 servings.

Summary of processes: Chop ¼ cup fresh parsley

Freeze in: 1-gallon bag; 1-quart bag

Serve with: Tropical fruit, crescent rolls

CHAPTER FOUR

MEXICAN CHICKEN LASAGNA

¾ cup chopped onion
3 14-ounce cans stewed tomatoes with juice
½ cup salsa, medium or mild
1 1¼-ounce package taco seasoning
1 16-ounce can black beans, rinsed and drained
1 large egg
16 ounces ricotta cheese
2 teaspoons minced garlic (2 cloves)
10 uncooked lasagna noodles
4 boneless, skinless cooked chicken breasts (about 1 pound) cut into
    1-inch cubes
1 4-ounce can chopped green chilies
1½ cups (about 6 ounces) grated Monterey Jack cheese

*T*o make sauce, combine chopped onion with tomatoes, salsa, and taco seasoning. Stir in beans.

To make ricotta layer, whisk egg in small bowl with a fork. Whisk in ricotta cheese and garlic.

Spread 1 cup tomato sauce mixture over the bottom of a greased 13x9x2-inch casserole dish (should barely cover bottom). Top with 5 (uncooked) noodles, overlapping slightly. Spread on one half of the ricotta cheese mixture. Sprinkle with half the chicken and half the chilies. Spoon 2 cups tomato sauce mixture on top, then add the rest of the ricotta cheese mixture; spread lightly. Sprinkle with half the grated cheese. Top with remaining noodles, chicken, chilies, tomato sauce mixture, and grated cheese. Cover with foil, label and freeze.

To prepare for serving, thaw and preheat oven to 350°. Bake, uncovered, for 40 minutes or until noodles are tender when pierced with sharp knife. Cool 10 minutes before serving. Makes 8 servings.

Summary of processes: Chop ¾ cup onion; mince 2 cloves garlic; cut 4 boneless, skinless cooked chicken breasts into 1-inch cubes; seed 4 ounces whole green chilies and slice into thin strips; grate 1½ cups Monterey jack cheese

Freeze in: 13x9x2-inch baking dish

Serve with: Slices of avocado and pink grapefruit on lettuce with poppyseed dressing

SOPA DE MAIZ

2 cups chicken broth
2 boneless, skinless cooked chicken breasts, chopped
1 16-ounce bag frozen corn
½ teaspoon cumin
1 teaspoon minced garlic (1 clove)
2 chicken bouillon cubes
1 4-ounce can diced green chilies
1 cup milk
Salt and pepper to taste
Fritos*
1 tomato, chopped*
1 avocado, chopped*
Salsa
Sour cream

*C*ombine first 7 ingredients in a 6-cup container and freeze.

When preparing to serve, thaw the soup and bring just to boiling. Add milk and simmer until soup is heated through. Season with salt and pepper.

In individual bowls, layer crushed Fritos, chopped tomatoes, and diced avocados. Then pour soup over all. Add dollop each of salsa and sour cream. Makes 5 to 6 servings.

Summary of processes: Chop 2 boneless, skinless cooked chicken breasts

Freeze in: 6-cup container

Serve with: Taco salad

BISCUIT BEEF BAKE

1 pound lean ground beef
½ cup onion, chopped
1 teaspoon minced garlic (1 clove)
1 14½ ounce can Mexican-style stewed tomatoes, undrained
1 15-ounce can black beans, rinsed and drained
1 8-ounce can tomato sauce
½ cup frozen corn
2 teaspoons chili powder
1 teaspoon cumin
1 teaspoon salt
1 12-ounce package Hungry Jack buttermilk biscuits*

*B*rown ground beef with the onion and garlic in a 10-inch skillet over medium heat until meat is no longer pink (or use 2½ cups already-browned ground beef). Stir in the remaining ingredients, except biscuits. Bring to a boil and simmer for 10 minutes. Cool. Package, label, and freeze. Store the tube of Hungry Jack biscuits in the refrigerator.

When preparing to serve, thaw and preheat oven to 400°. Transfer the mixture to an 8x8-inch ovenproof dish that has been treated with nonstick spray. Arrange the biscuits on top and bake for 15 to 20 minutes. Makes 6 servings.

Summary of processes: Chop ½ cup onion; mince 1 clove garlic

Freeze in: 5-cup container

Serve with: Baked apples

RECIPES

FRENCH STUFFED POTATOES

1 pound lean ground beef
¼ cup chopped green onion
1 4-ounce can mushroom stems and pieces
½ teaspoon salt
½ teaspoon onion salt
½ cup each grated Swiss and cheddar cheese
4 large baking potatoes*

*B*rown together in a skillet the ground beef, green onion, and mushrooms (add a tablespoon of water if mixture is too dry). Add the salt and onion salt.

Freeze the meat mixture in a freezer bag. Store the grated cheese in a small bag and slip the smaller bag into the larger one; store in freezer. Store the potatoes in the pantry (don't freeze raw potatoes).

When preparing to serve, thaw the meat mixture and cheeses. Preheat oven to 400°. Bake the potatoes for 1 hour or until done. When potatoes are nearly done, heat the meat mixture in a small saucepan or skillet.

Slice open the potatoes, break up potatoes with a fork, and spoon the meat mixture and cheese atop each potato. Return to the oven until cheese is melted. Makes 4 servings.

Summary of processes: Chop ¼ cup green onions; grate ½ cup cheddar cheese and ½ cup Swiss cheese.

Freeze in: 1-gallon bag; 1-quart bag

Serve with: Sliced tomatoes, Caesar salad